Listen to the Spirit—
He Will Lead You
2019 Prayer Journal

A Reflection Journal Calendar
with the thoughts of Servant of God
Catherine Doherty

Trinity Photography

Listen to the Spirit—He Will Lead You 2019 Prayer Journal

Scripture is taken from the Good News Translation with Deuterocanonicals/ Apocrypha - Second Edition (c) 1992.
American Bible Society
101 North Independence Mall East, Floor 8
Philadelphia, PA 19106-2155
www.americanbible.org.
Used with permission.

For information or **to order additional copies of this prayer journal,** contact:
**Trinity Photography
3805 7th St. NE #109
Great Falls, MT 59404-1154
1-888-220-5941
catholicprayerdiary@gmail.com
http://www.catholicprayerdiary.com**

Cover Photo: Whitetail deer in Crater Lake National Park, Oregon

ISBN: 978-0-9972772-1-0

Printed in South Korea.

DEDICATION

*We dedicate this work
to all those around the world
who are being martyred for their faith.
May their blood be the seed
of the conversion of many souls.*

CATHERINE DOHERTY, SERVANT OF GOD

Russian-born Catherine Doherty emigrated to Canada shortly after the Bolshevik Revolution. Though able to support herself and her family in a comfortable fashion, she heard the Lord calling her to live and work with the poor. He revealed to her what she later called "The Little Mandate" (see below). She responded to His call, and from that, Friendship House and the Madonna House Apostolates were born.

Catherine's faith in God was the center of her life. The Catholic Church is currently studying her for canonization, for her practice of heroic virtue during her lifetime. In 2002, she was declared "Servant of God." (For more on Catherine's life, see the books listed on the Acknowledgements page).

The continuing process of considering Catherine for canonization now requires that several miracles, attributed to her intercession, be reported and verified. The following prayer has been devised by the Madonna House staff for those wishing to ask Catherine to intercede for their intentions:

All loving Father, through Your beloved Son, Jesus, we have been taught to ask for what we need. And through His spouse, our Mother the Church, we have been instructed to pray for one another, and to ask the intercession of Your servants, who have fallen asleep in Christ. Therefore, through the intercession of Your servant, Catherine Doherty, we ask (here mention your petition). We ask this for Your honor and glory, and in the name of Jesus Christ, Your Son Our Lord. Amen.

Imprimatur:	Favors received may be sent to:
+J.R. Windle	Postulator, Madonna House
Bishop of Pembroke	2888 Dafoe Rd., RR 2, Combermere, Ontario
May 1, 1993	CANADA K0J 1L0

THE LITTLE MANDATE

Arise—go! Sell all you possess. Give it directly, personally to the poor. Take up My cross (their cross) and follow Me, going to the poor, being poor, being one with them, one with Me.

Little—be always little! Be simple, poor, childlike.

Preach the Gospel with your life—WITHOUT COMPROMISE! Listen to the Spirit. He will lead you.

Do little things exceedingly well for love of Me.

Love...love...love, never counting the cost.

Go into the marketplace and stay with Me. Pray, fast. Pray always, fast.

Be hidden. Be a light to your neighbor's feet. Go without fears into the depth of men's hearts. I shall be with you.

Pray always. I WILL BE YOUR REST.

WHAT DOES IT MEAN,
TO LIVE THE GOSPEL WITHOUT COMPROMISE?

To live the Gospel without compromise, to Catherine, meant to do everything that needs to be done in a day for love of God and for His glory. She called it doing the duty of the moment for Christ. That is how the most common folk among us, living the most ordinary and sometimes even tedious lives, can be heroes of Christian living! We can be modern-day martyrs! The word "martyr" does not mean "to die." It means "to give witness." To do everything God gives us to do—from peeling potatoes to helping our children with their homework to setting aside a regular time to pray each day, to suffering from an illness with a pleasant disposition, plus everything else our lives present for us to do—to do ALL to the best of our ability and in a loving way is to give witness to the goodness, love and glory of God. It will also lead us to do everything that involves others in a charitable way. Most of us are not called to do what the world considers "great things." Instead, we are called to do *all things* with *great love* for God and our neighbor. Do the duty of the moment for love of God, and you will help change the world!

CATHERINE ON

Preaching by Example

When I was growing up in Russia, my father was a diplomat. One time he and my mother gave a big, fancy tea party at our home for several hundred ambassadors and dignitaries. We were in the middle of having formal tea, with everyone using nice china and so forth. I was about nine years old at the time, and I was allowed to be there, all dressed up and carrying little cakes and being polite. Suddenly, the butler opened the door and announced to my father, "Christ is at the door." Well, the French ambassador's wife dropped her expensive teacup on the rug. She was not used to such interruptions!

Father excused himself, Mother excused herself, and off they went. And whom did they welcome? A hobo who had come to the door begging. And what did they do? My mother and father served him themselves even though we had fourteen servants in the house. My mother laid out the best linen, the most expensive silver and our best china and so forth, and she served a hobo. My father did likewise. I saw all of this and I wanted to serve the hobo too, but Mother said, "Oh no. You were not obedient last week; you cannot serve Christ unless you are obedient." So, in my little mind, to serve the poor was a great honor and a great joy.

from *Nazareth Family Spirituality*, pp. 39-40

ACKNOWLEDGEMENTS

We gratefully express our appreciation to Madonna House Publications for permission to quote from the following sources:

<u>by Catherine Doherty</u>:
  Beginning Again: Recovering Your Innocence and Joy through Confession, 2004
  Bogoroditza: She Who Gave Birth to God, 1998
  Dear Parents: A Gift of Love for Families, 1997
  Donkey Bells: Advent and Christmas, 1994
  Experience of God, An, 2002
  God in the Nitty-Gritty Life, 2002
  Gospel without Compromise, The, 1995
  Grace in Every Season: Through the Year with Catherine Doherty, 1992
  In the Footprints of Loneliness: Meditations—when you hear an echo in your heart, 2003
  In the Furnace of Doubts: Meditations—when you've lost your answers, 2002
  Kiss of Christ: Reflections on the Sacrament of Penance and Reconciliation, 1998
  Light in the Darkness: A Christian Vision for Unstable Times, 2009
  Living the Gospel without Compromise, 2002
  Molchanie: The Silence of God, 1991
  O Jesus: Prayers from the Diaries of Catherine DeHueck Doherty, 1996
  On the Cross of Rejection: Meditations—when your heart is pierced, 2003
  Poustinia: Encountering God in Silence, Solitude and Prayer, 2000
  Re-entry into Faith, undated booklet
  Season of Mercy: Lent and Easter, 1996
  Sobornost: Eastern Unity of Mind and Heart for Western Man, 1992
  The Stations of the Cross: In the Footsteps of the Passion, 2004
  Unfinished Pilgrimage: God's 'Little Mandate,' 1995
  Welcome, Pilgrim, 1991

<u>by others</u>:
  Fathering: Building the New Civilization of Love, 2000
  Mothering: Becoming the Heart of the Home, 2000
  Marriage: A Fountain of Grace, 2001

To obtain copies of these books and other works of Catherine Doherty and Madonna House Publications, or to obtain information regarding progress in Catherine's canonization cause, contact:

Madonna House Publications
2888 Dafoe Rd., RR 2
Combermere, Ontario, Canada K0J 1L0
1-888-703-7110
publications@madonnahouse.org
http://www.madonnahouse.org • http://www.catherinedoherty.org

KEEPING A PRAYER JOURNAL

One of the uses that can be made of this engagement calendar/diary is to keep a prayer journal. Keeping a prayer journal simply means to record your day's experiences, thoughts, interactions, etc., with an eye to the fact that God was part of your day. Through the recording of events, interactions, etc., you can consciously take the time to look for where God was in what others did for or said to you; and for where He was in what you did for or said to others. We each are called to be "God with skin on" to those around us, and to let them be the same to us. Journaling about your day can help you begin to look for Him and remain conscious of Him in the living of your ordinary, everyday life!

Or, you can write down thoughts about your day, your life, your relationships, your questions, your dreams, your disappointments, etc., each day as a "letter" to God. Address Him in what you say. Tell Him what's in your heart. Ask Him the hard questions that are puzzling you. Unburden your sorrows to Him. Ask His help. Share your joys with Him. In other words, grow in your awareness, through keeping a prayer journal, that God is with you each and every moment of each and every day; that He knows you personally and cares about you personally; that He loves you; and that He wants you to have a personal relationship with Him and love Him in return. As you spend time writing to Him, you will come to know more clearly that He is always there with you!

Listen to the Spirit—He Will Lead You makes an excellent prayer journal. It can also be used as an engagement calendar, a daily reminder/daily planner, a lesson plan book for teachers and home schoolers, a daily meditation aid, or anything else you might think of. It also makes an excellent gift for priests, sisters, RCIA candidates, teens being confirmed, volunteers, parish and school staff members, spouses and friends. The inspirational writings and daily Scripture verses contained in it are an aid for those who have an active faith life, as well as for those who are looking for something to help them find the Lord in their lives. Many of the people who use this book each year to assist them in their daily walk with the Lord find that it is true: if you "listen to the Spirit—He will lead you!"

NOTES ON CALENDAR CONTENTS

- Saints days, feasts and Church holy days follow the official Roman Catholic liturgical calendars for the United States and Canada.
- Colors for Mass vestments are given for each day.
- Holy Days of Obligation are noted.
- Solemnities are printed in **bold** text.
- Scripture readings listed for each day follow the Roman Catholic liturgical calendar of readings for Sunday Cycle C and Weekday Cycle 1, comprising the Mass readings for 2019.
- Each Scripture quote is taken from one of the readings for that day's Mass.
- Civic holidays are listed for both the United States and Canada.

2019

JANUARY

S	M	T	W	T	F	S
		1	2	3	4	5
6	7	8	9	10	11	12
13	14	15	16	17	18	19
20	21	22	23	24	25	26
27	28	29	30	31		

FEBRUARY

S	M	T	W	T	F	S
					1	2
3	4	5	6	7	8	9
10	11	12	13	14	15	16
17	18	19	20	21	22	23
24	25	26	27	28		

MARCH

S	M	T	W	T	F	S
					1	2
3	4	5	6	7	8	9
10	11	12	13	14	15	16
17	18	19	20	21	22	23
24	25	26	27	28	29	30
31						

APRIL

S	M	T	W	T	F	S
	1	2	3	4	5	6
7	8	9	10	11	12	13
14	15	16	17	18	19	20
21	22	23	24	25	26	27
28	29	30				

MAY

S	M	T	W	T	F	S
			1	2	3	4
5	6	7	8	9	10	11
12	13	14	15	16	17	18
19	20	21	22	23	24	25
26	27	28	29	30	31	

JUNE

S	M	T	W	T	F	S
						1
2	3	4	5	6	7	8
9	10	11	12	13	14	15
16	17	18	19	20	21	22
23	24	25	26	27	28	29
30						

JULY

S	M	T	W	T	F	S
	1	2	3	4	5	6
7	8	9	10	11	12	13
14	15	16	17	18	19	20
21	22	23	24	25	26	27
28	29	30	31			

AUGUST

S	M	T	W	T	F	S
				1	2	3
4	5	6	7	8	9	10
11	12	13	14	15	16	17
18	19	20	21	22	23	24
25	26	27	28	29	30	31

SEPTEMBER

S	M	T	W	T	F	S
1	2	3	4	5	6	7
8	9	10	11	12	13	14
15	16	17	18	19	20	21
22	23	24	25	26	27	28
29	30					

OCTOBER

S	M	T	W	T	F	S
		1	2	3	4	5
6	7	8	9	10	11	12
13	14	15	16	17	18	19
20	21	22	23	24	25	26
27	28	29	30	31		

NOVEMBER

S	M	T	W	T	F	S
					1	2
3	4	5	6	7	8	9
10	11	12	13	14	15	16
17	18	19	20	21	22	23
24	25	26	27	28	29	30

DECEMBER

S	M	T	W	T	F	S
1	2	3	4	5	6	7
8	9	10	11	12	13	14
15	16	17	18	19	20	21
22	23	24	25	26	27	28
29	30	31				

JANUARY 2019

Sunday	Monday	Tuesday	Wednesday	Thursday	Friday	Saturday
		1 New Year's Day **Mary, Mother of God**	2	3	4	5
6 Epiphany	7	8	9	10	11	12
13	14	15	16	17	18	19
20	21 Martin Luther King Day	22	23	24	25	26
27	28	29	30	31		

FEBRUARY 2019

Sunday	Monday	Tuesday	Wednesday	Thursday	Friday	Saturday
					1	2
3	4	5	6	7	8	9
10	11	12	13	14 Valentine's Day	15	16
17	18 Presidents' Day	19	20	21	22	23
24	25	26	27	28		

MARCH 2019

Sunday	Monday	Tuesday	Wednesday	Thursday	Friday	Saturday
					1	2
3	4	5	6 *Ash Wednesday*	7	8	9
10 *Daylight Savings Time Begins*	11	12	13	14	15	16
17	18	19	20 *First Day of Spring*	21	22	23
24 / 31	25	26	27	28	29	30

APRIL 2019

Sunday	Monday	Tuesday	Wednesday	Thursday	Friday	Saturday
	1	2	3	4	5	6
7	8	9	10	11	12	13
14 Palm Sunday	15	16	17	18 Holy Thursday	19 Good Friday	20 Holy Saturday
21 **Easter**	22	23	24	25	26	27
28 Divine Mercy Sunday	29	30				

MAY 2019

Sunday	Monday	Tuesday	Wednesday	Thursday	Friday	Saturday
			1	2	3	4
5	6	7	8	9	10	11
12 Mother's Day	13	14	15	16	17	18
19	20 Victoria Day *Canada*	21	22	23	24	25
26	27 Memorial Day	28	29	30 **Ascension** *(some of USA)*	31	

JUNE 2019

Sunday	Monday	Tuesday	Wednesday	Thursday	Friday	Saturday
						1
2 **Ascension** *(Canada and most of USA)*	3	4	5	6	7	8
9	10	11	12	13	14 Flag Day	15
16 Father's Day	17	18	19	20	21 *First Day of Summer*	22
23 / 30	24	25	26	27	28	29

JULY 2019

Sunday	Monday	Tuesday	Wednesday	Thursday	Friday	Saturday
	1 Canada Day *Canada*	2	3	4 Independence Day	5	6
7	8	9	10	11	12	13
14	15	16	17	18	19	20
21	22	23	24	25	26	27
28	29	30	31			

AUGUST 2019

Sunday	Monday	Tuesday	Wednesday	Thursday	Friday	Saturday
				1	2	3
4	5 Civic Holiday *Canada*	6	7	8	9	10
11	12	13	14	15 **Assumption** **of Mary**	16	17
18	19	20	21	22	23	24
25	26	27	28	29	30	31

SEPTEMBER 2019

Sunday	Monday	Tuesday	Wednesday	Thursday	Friday	Saturday
1	2 Labor Day *USA & Canada*	3	4	5	6	7
8	9	10	11	12	13	14
15	16	17	18	19	20	21
22	23 *First Day of Autumn*	24	25	26	27	28
29	30					

OCTOBER 2019

Sunday	Monday	Tuesday	Wednesday	Thursday	Friday	Saturday
		1	2	3	4	5
6	7	8	9	10	11	12
13	14 Columbus Day Observed Thanksgiving *Canada*	15	16	17	18	19
20	21	22	23	24	25	26
27	28	29	30	31 Halloween		

NOVEMBER 2019

Sunday	Monday	Tuesday	Wednesday	Thursday	Friday	Saturday
					1 All Saints Day	2 All Souls Day
3	4	5	6	7	8	9
10 *Daylight Savings Time Ends*	11 Veterans Day Remembrance Day *(Canada)*	12	13	14	15	16
17	18	19	20	21	22	23
24	25	26	27 Thanksgiving *USA*	28	29	30

DECEMBER 2019

Sunday	Monday	Tuesday	Wednesday	Thursday	Friday	Saturday
1	2	3	4	5	6	7
8	9 **Immaculate Conception**	10	11	12	13	14
15	16	17	18	19	20	21
22 *First Day of Winter*	23	24 Christmas Eve	25 **Christmas**	26 **Boxing Day** *Canada*	27	28
29	30	31 New Year's Eve				

A BROWN BEAR IN KENAI NATIONAL PARK, ALASKA

"To meet [Christ], we must be *awake* for Him. ... St. Paul calls us in a loud voice to arise from our sleep! Our salvation is nearer than we believed; ... This call of His means *now!* Today! Every day of the year, every hour of every day, is the hour for us to arise from our sleep."

from *Donkey Bells: Advent and Christmas*

Tuesday, January 1 NEW YEAR'S DAY   HOLY DAY OF OBLIGATION

SOLEMNITY OF MARY, THE HOLY MOTHER OF GOD *(White)*

"When the right time finally came, God sent His own Son [into the world]. He came as the son of a human mother." (Gal 4:4)

Num 6:22-27
Ps 67:2-3,5,6,8
Gal 4:4-7
Lk 2:16-21

Wednesday, January 2

STS. BASIL THE GREAT AND GREGORY NAZIANZEN,
BISHOPS AND DOCTORS *(White)*

"Christ has poured out His Spirit on you."
(1 Jn 2:27a)

1 Jn 2:22-28
Ps 98:1-4
Jn 1:19-28

Thursday, January 3

CHRISTMAS WEEKDAY *(White)*
THE MOST HOLY NAME OF JESUS *(White)*

"[The Father's] love is so great that we are
called God's children — and so, in fact, we
are." (1 Jn 3:1b)

1 Jn 2:29—3:6
Ps 98:1,3-6
Jn 1:29-34

Friday, January 4

USA: ST. ELIZABETH ANN SETON, WIFE, MOTHER, RELIGIOUS *(White)*

"If we...see others in need, yet close your hearts against them, how can we claim that we love God?" (1 Jn 3:17)

1 Jn 3:7-10
Ps 98:1,7-9
Jn 1:35-42

Saturday, January 5

USA: ST. JOHN NEUMANN, BISHOP *(White)*

"This is how we know what love is: Christ gave His life for us." (1 Jn 3:16a)

1 Jn 3:11-21
Ps 100:1-5
Jn 1:43-51

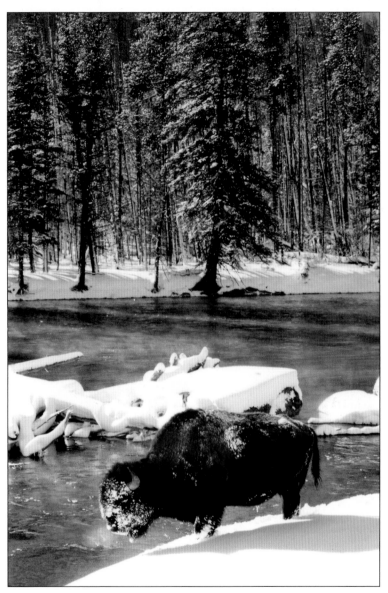

A BISON IN YELLOWSTONE NATIONAL PARK, WYOMING

"Remember that as Christians we are called to be apostles of the Good News continually, everywhere. We witness to Christ by our presence, by the way we sit, talk, eat. We evangelize at every second of the day and with each breath we take."

from *Living the Gospel without Compromise*

Sunday, January 6

THE EPIPHANY OF THE LORD *(White)*

"...on you the light of the LORD will shine; the brightness of His presence will be with you." (Is 60:2bc)

Is 60:1-6
Ps 72:1-2,7-8,10-11,12-13
Eph 3:2-3a, 5-6
Mt 2:1-12

Monday, January 7

CHRISTMAS WEEKDAY *(White)*
ST. RAYMOND OF PENYAFORT, PRIEST *(White)*
CANADA: ST. ANDRÉ BESSETTE, RELIGIOUS *(White)*

"You belong to God, my children..." (1 Jn 4:4a)

1 Jn 3:22—4:6
Ps 2:7-8,10-11
Mt 4:12-17,23-25

Tuesday, January 8

CHRISTMAS WEEKDAY *(White)*
CANADA: ST. RAYMOND OF PENYAFORT, PRIEST *(White)*

"God showed His love for us by sending His only Son into the world, so that we might have life through Him." (1 Jn 4:9)

1 Jn 4:7-10
Ps 72:1-4,7-8
Mk 6:34-44

Wednesday, January 9

CHRISTMAS WEEKDAY *(White)*

"There is no fear in love; perfect love drives out all fear."
(1 Jn 4:18a)

1 Jn 4:11-18
Ps 72:1-2,10,12-13
Mk 6:45-52

Thursday, January 10

CHRISTMAS WEEKDAY *(White)*

"Our love for God means that we obey His commands."
(1 Jn 5:3a)

1 Jn 4:19—5:4
Ps 72:1-2,14-15,17
Lk 4:14-22a

Friday, January 11

CHRISTMAS WEEKDAY *(White)*

"God has given us eternal life, and this life has its source in His Son. Whoever has the Son has this life." (1 Jn 5:11-12a)

1 Jn 5:5-13
Ps 147:12-15,19-20
Lk 5:12-16

Saturday, January 12

CHRISTMAS WEEKDAY *(White)*
CANADA: ST. MARGUERITE BOURGEOYS, VIRGIN *(White)*

"My children, keep yourselves safe from false gods!" (1 Jn 5:21)

1 Jn 5:14-21
Ps 149:1-6,9
Jn 3:22-30

WATERFALL IN JASPER NATIONAL PARK, CANADA

"Once we are baptized into the life and death of Jesus Christ, we receive a tremendous call to stewardship... There is a stewardship of the heart—my heart. I use the talents that God has given me to penetrate deeply into His laws. 'Master, which is the greatest commandment?' Jesus replied, 'You must love the Lord your God with all your heart, with all your soul, and with all your mind... The second resembles it: You must love your neighbor as yourself.' (Mt 22:37-39). What a tremendous stewardship because [as I become the steward of my heart in order to grow in God's law of love] I become like Him. Then, I open the door of His kingdom to others through my example."

from *Living the Gospel without Compromise*

Sunday, January 13

BAPTISM OF THE LORD *(White)*

"Through [My servant] I [the LORD] will make a covenant with all peoples; through [him] I will bring light to the nations." (Is 42:6cd)

Is 42:1-4,6-7 or Is 40:1-5,9-11
Ps 29:1-4,9-10
Acts 10:34-38 or Ti 2:11-14; 3:4-7
Lk 3:15-16,21-22

Monday, January 14

WEEKDAY *(Green)* - *1st Week in Ordinary Time*

"'The right time has come,' [Jesus] said, '...turn away from your sins and believe the Good News!'" (Mk 1:15)

Heb 1:1-6
Ps 97:1-2,6-7,9
Mk 1:14-20

Tuesday, January 15

WEEKDAY *(Green)*

"This man [Jesus] has authority to give orders to the evil spirits and they obey Him!" (Mk 1:27c)

Heb 2:5-12
Ps 8:2,5,6-9
Mk 1:21-28

Wednesday, January 16

WEEKDAY *(Green)*

"Be glad that we belong to [the LORD]; let all who worship Him rejoice." (Ps 105:3)

Heb 2:14-18
Ps 105:1-4,6-9
Mk 1:29-39

Thursday, January 17

ST. ANTHONY, ABBOT *(White)*

"Be careful that none of you have a heart so evil and unbelieving that you will turn away from the living God." (Heb 3:12)

Heb 3:7-14
Ps 95:6-11
Mk 1:40-45

Friday, January 18

WEEKDAY *(Green)*
WEEK OF PRAYER FOR CHRISTIAN UNITY BEGINS

"We will tell the next generation about the
LORD'S power and His great deeds..." (Ps 78:4b)

Heb 4:1-5,11
Ps 78:3-4,6-8
Mk 2:1-12

Saturday, January 19

WEEKDAY *(Green)*; BLESSED VIRGIN MARY *(White)*

"There is nothing that can be hid from God;
everything in all creation is exposed and open
before His eyes." (Heb 4:13ab)

Heb 4:12-16
Ps 19:8-10,15
Mk 2:13-17

AN ARTIC FOX NEAR CHURCHILL, MANITOBA, CANADA

"I saw the Lord hungry and cold and shelterless, I could not rest, I had to take Him into my arms and give Him comfort. But lo, when I did, it was not God but just a child hungry and cold."

from *An Experience of God*

Sunday, January 20

SECOND SUNDAY IN ORDINARY TIME *(Green)*

"The Spirit's presence is shown in some way in each person for the good of all." (1 Cor 12:7)

Is 62:1-5
Ps 96:1-3,7-10
1 Cor 12:4-11
Jn 2:1-11

Monday, January 21 MARTIN LUTHER KING DAY

ST. AGNES, VIRGIN AND MARTYR *(Red)*

"When [Jesus] was made perfect [in obedience], He became the source of eternal salvation for all those who obey Him." (Heb 5:9)

Heb 5:1-10
Ps 110:1-4
Mk 2:18-22

Tuesday, January 22

USA: DAY OF PRAYER FOR THE LEGAL PROTECTION
   OF UNBORN CHILDREN *(White or Violet)*
CANADA: ST. VINCENT, DEACON AND MARTYR *(Red)*

"We have...hope [in God] as an anchor for our lives." (Heb 6:19a)

Heb 6:10-20
Ps 111:1-2,4-5,9-10
Mk 2:23-28
Readings for the Day of Prayer: see Appendix

Wednesday, January 23

WEEKDAY *(Green)*; USA: ST. VINCENT, DEACON AND MARTYR *(Red)*
ST. MARIANNE COPE, VIRGIN *(White)*

"Jesus was angry...but at the same time felt sorry for [the people], because they were so stubborn and wrong." (Mk 3:5)

Heb 7:1-3,15-17
Ps 110:1-4
Mk 3:1-6

Thursday, January 24

ST. FRANCIS DE SALES, BISHOP AND DOCTOR *(White)*

"[Jesus] is able, now and always, to save those who come to God through Him..." (Heb 7:25)

Heb 7:25—8:6
Ps 40:7-10,17
Mk 3:7-12

Friday, January 25

CONVERSION OF ST. PAUL, APOSTLE *(White)*
Week of Prayer for Christian Unity Ends

"Whoever believes [the Gospel] and is baptized will be saved." (Mk 16:16a)

Acts 22:3-16 or Acts 9:1-22
Ps 117:1-2
Mk 16:15-18

Saturday, January 26

STS. TIMOTHY AND TITUS, BISHOPS *(White)*

"Do not be ashamed of witnessing for our Lord... Instead, take your part in suffering for the Good News, as God gives you the strength for it." (2 Tm 1:8)

2 Tm 1:1-8 or Ti 1:1-5
Ps 89:20-22,25-26
Mk 3:20-21

POLAR BEARS IN CHURCHILL, MANITOBA, CANADA

"[The glory of our Lord]...can be revealed in each one of us... All we need do is just to stop our personality clashes... judgmentalism... mistrust... anger... [and] ...hostility against one another. All we need do is to *begin to love one another as Christ loved us*. Then the pagans of today will say: 'Well now, look at those Christians, will you? They've really got something. See how they love one another!'"

from *Donkey Bells: Advent and Christmas*

Sunday, January 27

THIRD SUNDAY IN ORDINARY TIME *(Green)*

"Today is holy to our LORD, so do not be sad. The joy that the LORD gives you will make you strong." (Neh 8:10c)

Neh 8:2-4a,5-6,8-10
Ps 19:8-10,15
1 Cor 12:12-30
Lk 1:1-4; 4:14-21

Monday, January 28

ST. THOMAS AQUINAS, PRIEST AND DOCTOR *(White)*

"I [Jesus] assure you that people can be forgiven all their sins and all the evil things they may say." (Mk 3:28)

Heb 9:15,24-28
Ps 98:1-6
Mk 3:22-30

Tuesday, January 29

WEEKDAY *(Green)*

"...we are all purified from sin by the offering that [Jesus] made of His own body once and for all." (Heb 10:10b)

Heb 10:1-10
Ps 40:2,4,7-8,10-11
Mk 3:31-35

Wednesday, January 30

WEEKDAY *(Green)*

"The Holy Spirit...gives us His witness... 'I will put My laws in [repenters'] hearts and write them on their minds.'" (Heb 10:17)

Heb 10:11-18
Ps 110:1-4
Mk 4:1-20

Thursday, January 31

ST. JOHN BOSCO, PRIEST *(White)*

"The same rules you use to judge others will be used by God to judge you..." (Mk 4:24)

Heb 10:19-25
Ps 24:1-6
Mk 4:21-25

Friday, February 1

WEEKDAY *(Green)*

"You need to be patient, in order to do the will of God and receive what He promises." (Heb 10:36)

Heb 10:32-39
Ps 37:3-6,23-24,39-40
Mk 4:26-34

Saturday, February 2

PRESENTATION OF THE LORD *(White)*

"[Jesus] can help those who are tempted because He Himself was tempted and suffered." (Heb 2:18)

Mal 3:1-4
Ps 24:7-10
Heb 2:14-18
Lk 2:22-40

ADELIE PENGUINS IN ANTARCTICA

"For [Jesus] told us first to love God with all our hearts, with all our being, and then to love our neighbor as ourselves. ...He also said that 'by this shall all men know that you are My disciples, that you love one another as I have loved you.' Finally, He said, 'Love your enemies.'"

from *The Gospel without Compromise*

Sunday, February 3

FOURTH SUNDAY IN ORDINARY TIME *(Green)*

"These three remain: faith, hope and love; and the greatest of these is love." (1 Cor 13:13)

Jer 1:4-5,17-19
Ps 71:1-6,15-17
1 Cor 12:31—13:13
Lk 4:21-30

Monday, February 4

WEEKDAY *(Green)*

"Go back home to your family and tell them how much the Lord has done for you and how kind He has been to you." (Mk 5:19)

Heb 11:32-40
Ps 31:20-24
Mk 5:1-20

Tuesday, February 5

ST. AGATHA, VIRGIN AND MARTYR *(Red)*

"Jesus...[said], 'Don't be afraid, only believe.'" (Mk 5:36b)

Heb 12:1-4
Ps 22:26-28,30-32
Mk 5:21-43

Wednesday, February 6

ST. PAUL MIKI AND COMPANIONS, MARTYRS *(Red)*

"Try to be at peace with everyone, and try to live a holy life, because no one will see the Lord without it." (Heb 12:14)

Heb 12:4-7,11-15
Ps 103:1-2,13-14,17-18
Mk 6:1-6

Thursday, February 7

WEEKDAY *(Green)*

"...O God, we think of Your constant love." (Ps 48:9)

Heb 12:18-19,21-24
Ps 48:2-4,9-11
Mk 6:7-13

Friday, February 8

WEEKDAY *(Green)*; ST. JEROME EMILIANI, PRIEST *(White)*
ST. JOSEPHINE BAKHITA, VIRGIN *(White)*

"Marriage is to be honored by all, and husbands and wives must be faithful to each other."
(Heb 13:4)

Heb 13:1-8
Ps 27:1,3,5,8-9
Mk 6:14-29

Saturday, February 9

WEEKDAY *(Green)*; BLESSED VIRGIN MARY *(White)*

"May the God of peace provide you with every good thing you need in order to do His will..."
(Heb 13:20-21)

Heb 13:15-17,20-21
Ps 23:1-6
Mk 6:30-34

WOLVES NEAR SANDSTONE, MINNESOTA

"Friendship needs to be open-ended, not a closed circle. For example, a little group of people get very close and are sitting at a table. Let's say that you walk up to this table [and say], 'Hi, how's everything?' And you meet with an 'Okay.' 'Well, how have you been?' 'Fine.' 'What kind of things have you been doing?' The cold that comes from those people is Arctic; you feel rejected. That kind of friendship is closed unto itself totally, but if you walk up and they say, 'Sit down, join us,' it's open-ended, not exclusive."

from *Mystical Body of Christ*

Sunday, February 10

FIFTH SUNDAY IN ORDINARY TIME *(Green)*

"The LORD Almighty is holy! His glory fills the world." (Is 6:3)

Is 6:1-2a,3-8
Ps 138:1-5,7-8
1 Cor 15:1-11
Lk 5:1-11

Monday, February 11

WEEKDAY *(Green)*
OUR LADY OF LOURDES *(White)*

"In the beginning...God created the universe."
(Gen 1:1)

Gen 1:1-19
Ps 104:1-2,5-6,10,12,24,35
Mk 6:53-56

Tuesday, February 12

WEEKDAY *(Green)*

"Jesus [said to the Pharisees], 'You have a clever way of rejecting God's law in order to uphold your own teaching.'" (Mk 7:9)

Gen 1:20—2:4a
Ps 8:4-9
Mk 7:1-13

Wednesday, February 13

WEEKDAY *(Green)*

"[F]rom your heart come the evil ideas which lead you to do immoral things..." (Mk 7:21)

Gen 2:4b-9,15-17
Ps 104:1-2,27-30
Mk 7:14-23

Thursday, February 14 VALENTINE'S DAY

STS. CYRIL, MONK, AND METHODIUS, BISHOP *(White)*

"...a man leaves his father and mother and is united with his wife, and they become one." (Gen 2:24)

Gen 2:18-25
Ps 128:1-5
Mk 7:24-30

Friday, February 15

WEEKDAY *(Green)*

"You are my hiding place, [O LORD]; You will
save me from trouble." (Ps 32:7)

Gen 3:1-8
Ps 32:1-2,5-7
Mk 7:31-37

Saturday, February 16

WEEKDAY *(Green)*; BLESSED VIRGIN MARY *(White)*

"Teach us how short our life is, [O LORD], so that
we may become wise." (Ps 90:12)

Gen 3:9-24
Ps 90:2-6,12-13
Mk 8:1-10

A BARRED OWL NEAR ELY, MINNESOTA

"Knowledge is given to men and women for one purpose only: that man might love God and serve Him."

from *Light in the Darkness: A Christian Vision for Unstable Times*

Sunday, February 17

SIXTH SUNDAY IN ORDINARY TIME *(Green)*

"The truth is that Christ has been raised from death, as the guarantee that those who sleep in death will also be raised." (1 Cor 15:20)

Jer 17:5-8
Ps 1:1-6
1 Cor 15:12,16-20
Lk 6:17,20-26

Monday, February 18 PRESIDENTS' DAY

LENTEN WEEKDAY *(Violet)*

"...sin is crouching at your door. It wants to rule you, but you must overcome it." (Gen 4:7)

Gen 4:1-15,25
Ps 50:1,8,16-17,20-21
Mk 8:11-13

Tuesday, February 19

WEEKDAY *(Green)*

"Praise the LORD ... praise His glory and power."
(Ps 29:1)

Gen 6:5-8; 7:1-5,10
Ps 29:1-4,9-10
Mk 8:14-21

Wednesday, February 20

WEEKDAY *(Green)*

"As long as the world exists, there will be a time for planting and a time for harvest." (Gen 8:22a)

Gen 8:6-13,20-22
Ps 116:12-15,18-19
Mk 8:22-26

Thursday, February 21

WEEKDAY *(Green)*
ST. PETER DAMIAN, BISHOP AND DOCTOR *(White)*

"Write down for the coming generation what the LORD has done, so that people not yet born will praise Him." (Ps 102:18)

Gen 9:1-13
Ps 102:16-23,29
Mk 8:27-33

Friday, February 22

THE CHAIR OF ST. PETER THE APOSTLE *(White)*

"[Jesus said to Peter]... 'Whatever you prohibit on earth will be prohibited in heaven, and what you permit on earth will be permitted in heaven.'" (Mt 16:19)

1 Pt 5:1-4
Ps 23:1-6
Mt 16:13-19

Saturday, February 23

ST. POLYCARP, BISHOP AND MARTYR *(Red)*

"To have faith is to be sure of the things we hope for, to be certain of the things we cannot see." (Heb 11:1)

Heb 11:1-7
Ps 145:2-5,10-11
Mk 9:2-13

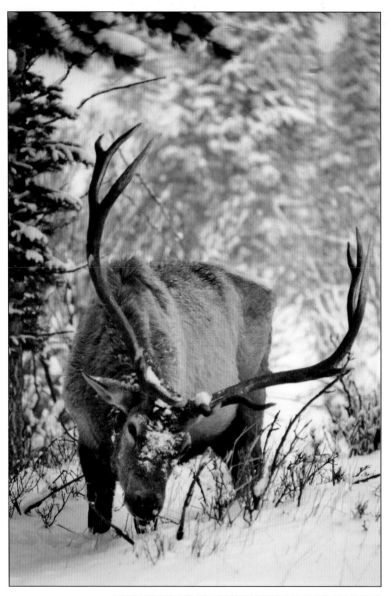

A BULL ELK IN YELLOWSTONE NATIONAL PARK, WYOMING

"People hunger for God as they never hungered before. They hunger for belief in Him, but cannot come to this belief if no one shows them how to love God."

from *Re-entry into Faith*

Sunday, February 24

SEVENTH SUNDAY IN ORDINARY TIME *(Green)*

"Love your enemies and do good to them... You will then have a great reward and you will be children of the Most High God. For He is good to the ungrateful and the wicked. Be merciful just as your Father is merciful." (Lk 6:35-36)

1 Sam 26:2,7-9,12-13,22-23
Ps 103:1-4,8,10,12-13
1 Cor 15:45-49
Lk 6:27-38

Monday, February 25

WEEKDAY *(Green)*

"I do have faith [Lord], but not enough. Help me have more!" (Mk 9:24)

Sir 1:1-10
Ps 93:1-2,5
Mk 9:14-29

Tuesday, February 26

WEEKDAY *(Green)*

"Accept whatever happens to you. Even if you suffer humiliation, be patient. Gold is tested by fire, and human character is tested in the furnace of humiliation. Trust the Lord..." (Sir 2:4-6a)

Sir 2:1-11
Ps 37:3-4,18-19,27-28,39-40
Mk 9:30-37

Wednesday, February 27

WEEKDAY *(Green)*

"Put your trust in Wisdom, and you will possess her and pass her on to your descendants."
(Sir 4:16)

Sir 4:11-19
Ps 119:165,168,171,172,174,175
Mk 9:38-40

Thursday, February 28

WEEKDAY *(Green)*

"Don't rely on money to make you independent ...[or]...think you have to have everything you want...[or]...think that no one can exercise authority over you; [for] the Lord is certain to punish you." (Sir 8:1-3)

Sir 5:1-8
Ps 1:1-2,3,4,6
Mk 9:41-50

Friday, March 1

LENTEN WEEKDAY *(Violet)*

"A loyal friend is like a safe shelter; find one and you have found a treasure." (Sir 6:14)

Sir 6:5-17
Ps 119:12,16,18,27,34,35
Mk 10:1-12

Saturday, March 2

WEEKDAY *(Green)*; BLESSED VIRGIN MARY *(White)*

"Then the Lord formed human beings from the dust...[and]...made them to be like Himself... [and]...showed them the differece between good and evil." (Sir 17:1a,3a,7b)

Sir 17:1-15
Ps 103:13-14,15-16,17-18
Mk 10:13-16

AT A WATERING HOLE IN NAMIBIA, AFRICA

"Christ told us to love one another as He loved us. We too are called to love all men and women: those we like, those we dislike, even those who wish us evil."

from *Light in the Darkness: A Christian Vision for Unstable Times*

Sunday, March 3

EIGHTH SUNDAY IN ORDINARY TIME *(Green)*

"Why do you look at the speck in your brother's eye but pay no attention to the log in your own eye? ...You hypocrite! First take the log out of your own eye and then you will be able to see clearly to take the speck out of your brother's eye." (Lk 6:41,42bcd)

Sir 27:4-7
Ps 92:2-3,13-14,15-16
1 Cor 15:54-58
Lk 6:39-45

Monday, March 4

WEEKDAY *(Green)*
ST. CASIMIR *(White)*

"The Lord will allow those who repent to return to Him. He always gives encouragement to those who are losing hope." (Sir 17:24)

Sir 17:20-24
Ps 32:1-2,5,6,7
Mk 10:17-27

Tuesday, March 5

LENTEN WEEKDAY *(Violet)*

"Give to the Most High as He has given to you, just as generously as you can. The Lord always repays and will do it many times over." (Sir 35:10-11)

Sir 35:1-12
Ps 50:5-6,7-8,14,23
Mk 10:28-31

Wednesday, March 6

ASH WEDNESDAY

"When you [fast], wash your face and comb your hair so that...only your Father...will know [and He] will reward you." (Mt 6:17-18)

Jl 2:12-18
Ps 51:3-6,12-14,17
2 Cor 5:20—6:2
Mt 6:1-6,16-18

Thursday, March 7

THURSDAY AFTER ASH WEDNESDAY *(Violet)*
STS. PERPETUA AND FELICITY, MARTYRS

"I am now giving you the choice between life and death, between God's blessing and God's curse... Choose life." (Dt 30:19)

Dt 30:15-20
Ps 1:1-4,6
Lk 9:22-25

Friday, March 8

FRIDAY AFTER ASH WEDNESDAY *(Violet)*
ST. JOHN OF GOD, RELIGIOUS

"When you pray, I will answer you... if you put an end to oppression, to every gesture of contempt, and to every evil word." (Is 58:9a)

Is 58:1-9a
Ps 51:3-6,18-19
Mt 9:14-15

Saturday, March 9

SATURDAY AFTER ASH WEDNESDAY *(Violet)*
ST. FRANCES OF ROME, WIFE, MOTHER, RELIGIOUS

"If you give food to the hungry and satisfy those who are in need, then the darkness around you will turn to the brightness of noon." (Is 58:10)

Is 58:9b-14
Ps 86:1-6
Lk 5:27-32

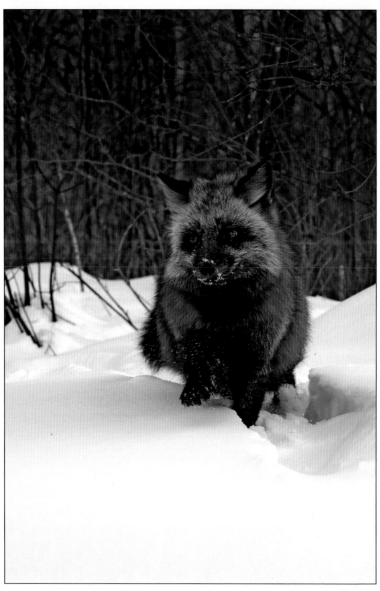

A CROSS FOX NEAR SANDSTONE, MINNESOTA

"Can I sleep when my brother has nowhere to lay his head? Can I eat my fill when my brother is hungry? Drink when he is thirsty? Clothe myself in fine raiments when he is naked, enjoy my freedom when he languishes in captivity; let him be sick and dying and not minister to him?"

from *Mystical Body of Christ*

Sunday, March 10 *Daylight Savings Time Begins*

FIRST SUNDAY OF LENT *(Violet)*

"God is the same Lord of all and richly blesses all who call to Him." (Rom 10:12b)

Dt 26:4-10
Ps 91:1-2,10-15
Rom 10:8-13
Lk 4:1-13

Monday, March 11

LENTEN WEEKDAY *(Violet)*

"Do not bear a grudge against others, but settle
your differences with them, so that you will not
commit sin because of them." (Lv 19:17)

Lv 19:1-2,11-18
Ps 19:8-10,15
Mt 25:31-46

Tuesday, March 12

LENTEN WEEKDAY *(Violet)*

"The LORD is near to those who are discouraged;
He saves those who have lost all hope." (Ps 34:18)

Is 55:10-11
Ps 34:4-7,16-19
Mt 6:7-15

Wednesday, March 13

LENTEN WEEKDAY *(Violet)*

"Everyone must pray earnestly to God and must give up their wicked behavior and their evil actions." (Jon 3:8b)

Jon 3:1-10
Ps 51:3-4,12-13,18-19
Lk 11:29-32

Thursday, March 14

LENTEN WEEKDAY *(Violet)*

"Do for others what you want them to do for you." (Mt 7:12a)

Est C:12,14-16,23-25
Ps 138:1-3,7-8
Mt 7:7-12

Friday, March 15

LENTEN WEEKDAY *(Violet)*

"'Do you think I enjoy seeing evil people die?' asks the Sovereign LORD. 'No, I would rather see them repent and live.'" (Ez 18:23)

Ez 18:21-28
Ps 130:1-8
Mt 5:20-26

Saturday, March 16

LENTEN WEEKDAY *(Violet)*

"Love your enemies and pray for those who persecute you..." (Mt 5:44)

Dt 26:16-19
Ps 119:1-2,4-5,7-8
Mt 5:43-48

CRATER LAKE NATIONAL PARK, OREGON

"How passing is the moment of sin; how eternal is Your peace. Why must we sin? Why do we sin when Your beauty is so complete? What is there even in the best the world has to offer to attract a soul who has caught a glimpse of You? ...I see again and again I fail You, Beloved. And yet You pursue me and bring me back. Why?"

from *O Jesus: Prayers from the Diaries of Catherine DeHueck Doherty*

Sunday, March 17

SECOND SUNDAY OF LENT *(Violet)*

"[T]here are many whose lives make them enemies of Christ's death on the cross... They are proud of what they should be ashamed of, and they think only of things that belong to this world." (Phil 3:18,19cd)

Gen 15:5-12,17-18
Ps 27:1,7-9,13-14
Phil 3:17—4:1
Lk 9:28b-36

Monday, March 18

LENTEN WEEKDAY *(Violet)*
ST. CYRIL OF JERUSALEM, BISHOP AND DOCTOR

"The measure [of generosity] you use for others
is the one that God will use for you." (Lk 6:38c)

Dan 9:4b-10
Ps 79:8-9,11,13
Lk 6:36-38

Tuesday, March 19

ST JOSEPH, SPOUSE OF THE BLESSED VIRGIN MARY *(White)*
  Principal Patron of Canada

"[Mary] will have a son, and you [Joseph] will
name Him Jesus—because He will save His
people from their sins." (Mt 1:21)

2 Sam 7:4-5a,12-14a,16
Ps 89:2-5,27-29
Rom 4:13,16-18,22
Mt 1:16,18-21,24a or Lk 2:41-51a

Wednesday, March 20 *First Day of Spring*

LENTEN WEEKDAY *(Violet)*

"...if one of you wants to be great, you must be the servant of the rest...like the Son of Man, who...[came] to serve..." (Mt 20:26b,27)

Jer 18:18-20
Ps 31:5-6,14-16
Mt 20:17-28

Thursday, March 21

LENTEN WEEKDAY *(Violet)*

"I, the LORD, search the minds and test the hearts of people. I treat each of them according to the way they live..." (Jer 17:10)

Jer 17:5-10
Ps 1:1-4,6
Lk 16:19-31

Friday, March 22

LENTEN WEEKDAY *(Violet)*

"The Kingdom of God will be taken away from [those who reject it] and given to...people who will produce the proper fruits." (Mt 21:43)

Gen 37:3-4,12-13a,17b-28a
Ps 105:16-21
Mt 21:33-43,45-46

Saturday, March 23

LENTEN WEEKDAY *(Violet)*
ST. TURIBIUS OF MOGROVEJO, BISHOP

"You, [O LORD], will be merciful to us once again. You will trample our sins underfoot and send them to the bottom of the sea!" (Mi 7:19)

Mi 7:14-15,18-20
Ps 103:1-4,9-12
Lk 15:1-3,11-32

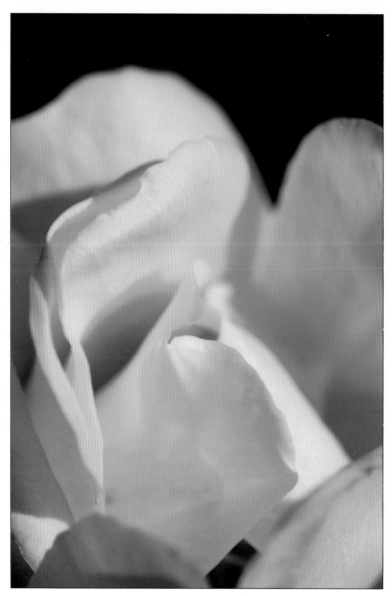

A ROSE IN NORTHEASTERN ILLINOIS

"Long before Jesus went to Gethsemane and stumbled under the weight of the cross, an angel appeared to an unassuming young woman, and prostrating himself before her, he announced to her that she was chosen by God to bear His Son. The angel said, 'Hail full of grace, the Lord is with you' (Lk 1:28), the introduction to the prayer known across the world."

from *On the Cross of Rejection: Meditations—when your heart is pierced*

Sunday, March 24

THIRD SUNDAY OF LENT *(Violet)*

"The LORD is merciful and loving, slow to become angry and full of constant love." (Ps 103:8)

Ex 3:1-8a,13-15
Ps 103:1-4,6-8,11
1 Cor 10:1-6,10-12
Lk 13:1-9

Monday, March 25

THE ANNUNCIATION OF THE LORD *(White)*

"How I love to do Your will, my God! I keep Your teaching in my heart." (Ps 40:8)

Is 7:10-14; 8:10
Ps 40:7-11
Heb 10:4-10
Lk 1:26-38

Tuesday, March 26

LENTEN WEEKDAY *(Violet)*

"'Lord, if my brother keeps on sinning against me, how many times do I have to forgive him?' [Jesus answered,] ...'seventy times seven [times] ...'" (Mt 18:21-22)

Dan 3:25,34-43
Ps 25:4-9
Mt 18:21-35

Wednesday, March 27

LENTEN WEEKDAY *(Violet)*

"No other nation...has a god who is so near when they need Him as the LORD our God is to us." (Dt 4:7a)

Dt 4:1,5-9
Ps 147:12-13,15-16,19-20
Mt 5:17-19

Thursday, March 28

LENTEN WEEKDAY *(Violet)*

"The LORD said... 'I told [My people] to live the way I had commanded them, so that things would go well for them.'" (Jer 7:23b)

Jer 7:23-28
Ps 95:1-2,6-9
Lk 11:14-23

Friday, March 29

LENTEN WEEKDAY *(Violet)*

"Return...and let this prayer be your offering to [the LORD]: 'Forgive all our sins, accept our prayer, and we will praise You...'" (Hos 14:2)

Hos 14:2-10
Ps 81:6-11,14,17
Mk 12:28-34

Saturday, March 30

LENTEN WEEKDAY *(Violet)*

"What I [the LORD] want from you is plain and clear: I want your constant love..." (Hos 6:5b-6a)

Hos 6:1-6
Ps 51:3-4,18-21
Lk 18:9-14

ARCHES NATIONAL PARK, UTAH

"Repentance calls for a complete breakdown of pride, of self-assurance, of prestige that comes from success, of the innermost citadel of self-will."

from *Living the Gospel without Compromise*

Sunday, March 31

FOURTH SUNDAY OF LENT *(Violet or Rose)*

"...God...through Christ changed us from enemies into His friends and gave us the task of making others His friends also." (2 Cor 5:18)

Jos 5:9a,10-12
Ps 34:2-7
2 Cor 5:17-21
Lk 15:1-3,11-32

Monday, April 1

LENTEN WEEKDAY *(Violet)*

"I [the LORD] am making a new earth and new heavens. The events of the past will be completely forgotten." (Is 65:17)

Is 65:17-21
Ps 30:2,4-6,11-13
Jn 4:43-54

Tuesday, April 2

LENTEN WEEKDAY *(Violet)*
ST. FRANCIS OF PAOLA, HERMIT

"We will not be afraid, even if the earth is shaken and mountains fall into the ocean depths." (Ps 46:2)

Ez 47:1-9,12
Ps 46:1-3,5-6,8-9
Jn 5:1-16

Wednesday, April 3

LENTEN WEEKDAY *(Violet))*

"Even if a mother should forget her child, I [God] will never forget you." (Is 49:15b)

Is 49:8-15
Ps 145:8-9,13-14,17-18
Jn 5:17-30

Thursday, April 4

LENTEN WEEKDAY *(Violet)*
ST. ISIDORE OF SEVILLE, BISHOP AND DOCTOR

"You like to receive praise from one another, but you do not try to win praise from the One who alone is God." (Jn 5:44)

Ex 32:7-14
Ps 106:19-23
Jn 5:31-47

Friday, April 5

LENTEN WEEKDAY *(Violet)*
ST. VINCENT FERRER, PRIEST

"Good people suffer many troubles, but the
LORD saves them from them all." (Ps 34:19)

Wis 2:1a,12-22
Ps 34:17-21,23
Jn 7:1-2,10,25-30

Saturday, April 6

LENTEN WEEKDAY *(Violet)*

"God is my protector; He saves those who obey
Him." (Ps 7:10)

Jer 11:18-20
Ps 7:2-3,9-12
Jn 7:40-53

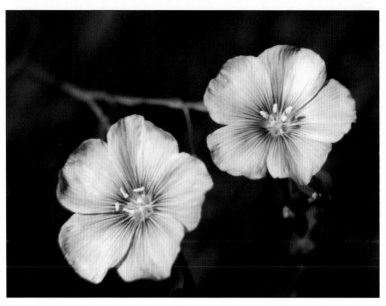

WILDFLOWERS IN GRAND TETON NATIONAL PARK, WYOMING

"So if anyone of us sins again, let us be peaceful about it, sorrowful, sad, but also filled with gratitude that we are able to say, 'Lord, have mercy.' Then we receive His mercy. ...That doesn't mean that we should go around saying, 'Well, because He's merciful, I'm going to sin.' No! On the contrary, [we should say], 'Because He's merciful, I shall be merciful.'"

from *Kiss of Christ: Reflections on the Sacrament of Penance and Reconciliation*

Sunday, April 7

FIFTH SUNDAY OF LENT *(Violet)*

"The LORD says, 'Do not cling to events of the past, or dwell on what happened long ago. Watch for the new thing I am going to do. It is happening already—you can see it now!'" (Is 43:18-19a)

Is 43:16-21
Ps 126:1-6
Phil 3:8-14
Jn 8:1-11

Monday, April 8

LENTEN WEEKDAY *(Violet)*

"Even if I go through the deepest darkness, I will not be afraid, LORD, for You are with me. Your shepherd's rod and staff protect me." (Ps 23:4)

Dan 13:1-9,15-17,19-30,33-62
Ps 23:1-6
Jn 8:1-11

Tuesday, April 9

LENTEN WEEKDAY *(Violet)*

"When I am in trouble, [LORD], don't turn away from me! Listen...and answer me quickly when I call!" (Ps 102:2)

Num 21:4-9
Ps 102:2-3,16-21
Jn 8:21-30

Wednesday, April 10

LENTEN WEEKDAY *(Violet)*

"'If you obey My teaching, you are really My disciples,' [Jesus told them]." (Jn 8:31)

Dan 3:14-20,91-92,95
(Ps) Dan 3:52-56
Jn 8:31-42

Thursday, April 11

LENTEN WEEKDAY *(Violet)*
ST. STANISLAUS, BISHOP AND MARTYR

"I will be your God and the God of your descendants." (Gen 17:7b)

Gen 17:3-9
Ps 105:4-9
Jn 8:51-59

Friday, April 12

LENTEN WEEKDAY *(Violet)*

"My God is my protection, and with Him I am safe." (Ps 18:2b)

Jer 20:10-13
Ps 18:2-7
Jn 10:31-42

Saturday, April 13

LENTEN WEEKDAY *(Violet)*
ST. MARTIN I, POPE AND MARTYR

"[The LORD says], 'I will comfort [My people] and turn their mourning into joy, their sorrow into gladness.'" (Jer 31:13c)

Ez 37:21-28
(Ps) Jer 31:10-13
Jn 11:45-56

YELLOWSTONE NATIONAL PARK, WYOMING

"To be childlike means not seeking to evade Calvary. Many times in our lives God gives us the grace to catch a glimpse of His reality—[that He is] someone who loved us first. We must respond to that love by *loving Him back.*"

from *Grace in Every Season: Through the Year with Catherine Doherty*

Sunday, April 14 · PALM SUNDAY

PALM SUNDAY OF THE PASSION OF THE LORD *(Red)*

"[Christ Jesus] was humble and walked the path of obedience all the way to death—death on the cross." (Phil 2:8)

Lk 19:28-40
Is 50:4-7
Ps 22:8-9,17-20,23-24
Phil 2:6-11
Lk 22:14—23:56

Monday, April 15

MONDAY OF HOLY WEEK *(Violet)*

"Trust in the LORD. Have faith, do not despair.
Trust in the LORD." (Ps 27:14)

Is 42:1-7
Ps 27:1-3,13-14
Jn 12:1-11

Tuesday, April 16

TUESDAY OF HOLY WEEK *(Violet)*

"I can trust the LORD to defend my cause; He
will reward me for what I do." (Is 49:4c)

Is 49:1-6
Ps 71:1-6,15,17
Jn 13:21-33,36-38

Wednesday, April 17

WEDNESDAY OF HOLY WEEK *(Violet)*

"Every morning [the Sovereign LORD] makes me
eager to hear what He is going to teach me."
(Is 50:4b)

Is 50:4-9a
Ps 69:8-10,21-22,31,33-34
Mt 26:14-25

Thursday, April 18 HOLY THURSDAY

THURSDAY OF HOLY WEEK

"...Jesus...took...bread, gave thanks to God, broke
it and said, 'This is My body, which is for you.
Do this in memory of Me.'" (1 Cor 11:23b-24)

Chrism Mass *(White)*
Is 61:1-3a,6a,8b-9
Ps 89:21-22,25,27
Rv 1:5-8
Lk 4:16-21

Mass of the Lord's Supper *(White)*
Ex 12:1-8,11-14
Ps 116:12-13,15-18
1 Cor 11:23-26
Jn 13:1-15

Friday, April 19 GOOD FRIDAY

FRIDAY OF THE PASSION OF THE LORD *(Red)*

"We are healed by the punishment he suffered, made whole by the blows he received." (Is 53:5)

Is 52:13—53:12
Ps 31:2,6,12-13,15-17,25
Heb 4:14-16; 5:7-9
Jn 18:1—19:42

Saturday, April 20 HOLY SATURDAY

HOLY SATURDAY *(White)*

"By our baptism...we were buried with [Christ]... in order that, just as Christ was raised from death by...the Father, so also we might live a new life." (Rom 6:4)

Easter Vigil Readings: see Appendix

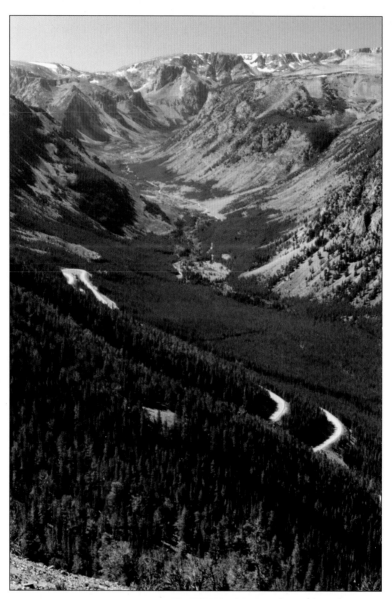

BEARTOOTH HIGHWAY (U.S. 212) IN MONTANA

"Easter is the feast of living, glorious Love, who walks among us until the end of time and who reigns in heaven without beginning or end, waiting for us to enjoy it for eternity, if only we make the lessons of its 'school of love' our own during our short exile on this earth."

from *Dear Parents: A Gift of Love for Families*

Sunday, April 21 EASTER

EASTER SUNDAY OF THE RESURRECTION OF THE LORD *(White)*

"You have been raised to life with Christ, so set your hearts on the things that are in heaven, where Christ sits on His throne on the right side of God. Keep your minds fixed on things there..." (Col 3:1-2a)

Acts 10:34a,37-43
Ps 118:1-2,16-17,22-23
Col 3:1-4 or 1 Cor 5:6b-8
Jn 20:1-9 or Lk 24:1-12

Monday, April 22

MONDAY WITHIN THE OCTAVE OF EASTER *(White))*

"[The Lord] is near me, and I will not be troubled. And so I am filled with gladness, and my words are full of joy." (Acts 2:25b-26ab)

Acts 2:14,22-33
Ps 16:1-2,5,7-11
Mt 28:8-15

Tuesday, April 23

TUESDAY WITHIN THE OCTAVE OF EASTER *(White)*

"All...are to know for sure that...Jesus...is the one that God has made Lord and Messiah!" (Acts 2:36)

Acts 2:36-41
Ps 33:4-5,18-20,22
Jn 20:11-18

Wednesday, April 24

WEDNESDAY WITHIN THE OCTAVE OF EASTER *(White)*

"Be glad that we belong to [the LORD]; let all who worship Him rejoice." (Ps 105:3)

Acts 3:1-10
Ps 105:1-4,6-9
Lk 24:13-35

Thursday, April 25

THURSDAY WITHIN THE OCTAVE OF EASTER *(White)*

"Repent...and turn to God, so that He will forgive your sins. If you do, times of spiritual strength will come from the Lord..." (Acts 3:19-20a)

Acts 3:11-26
Ps 8:2-9
Lk 24:35-48

Friday, April 26

FRIDAY WITHIN THE OCTAVE OF EASTER *(White)*

"Give thanks to the LORD, because He is good, and His love is eternal." (Ps 118:1)

Acts 4:1-12
Ps 118:1-2,4,22-27
Jn 21:1-14

Saturday, April 27

SATURDAY WITHIN THE OCTAVE OF EASTER *(White)*

"'Whoever believes [in the gospel] and is baptized will be saved,' [Jesus said]." (Mk 16:15)

Acts 4:13-21
Ps 118:1,14-21
Mk 16:9-15

BROWN BEAR CUBS IN KENAI NATIONAL PARK, ALASKA

"We are called to love one another, and that means first forgiving ourselves and everybody else. In order to love, one needs to forgive. For one cannot love the object of hostility, anger, hatred... [without] forgiveness. That demands mercy and compassion. 'Blessed are the merciful: they shall have mercy shown them' (Mt 5:7)."

from *Living the Gospel without Compromise*

Sunday, April 28 DIVINE MERCY SUNDAY

SECOND SUNDAY OF EASTER *(White)*

"Jesus said to [His disciples]... 'Peace be with you... If you forgive people's sins, they are forgiven; if you do not forgive them, they are not forgiven." (Jn 20:21a,23)

Acts 5:12-16
Ps 118:2-4,13-15,22,24
Rv 1:9-11a,12-13,17-19
Jn 20:19-31

Monday, April 29

ST. CATHERINE OF SIENA, VIRGIN AND DOCTOR *(White)*

"And now, Lord, ...allow us, Your servants, to speak Your message with all boldness." (Acts 4:29)

Acts 4:23-31
Ps 2:1-9
Jn 3:1-8

Tuesday, April 30

EASTER WEEKDAY *(White)*; ST. PIUS V, POPE *(White)*
CANADA: BLESSED MARIE DE L'INCARNATION, RELIGIOUS *(White)*

"The group of believers was one in mind and heart." (Acts 4:32a)

Acts 4:32-37
Ps 93:1-2,5
Jn 3:7b-15

Wednesday, May 1

EASTER WEEKDAY *(White)*; USA: ST. JOSEPH THE WORKER *(White)*
CANADA: ST. PIUS V, POPE

"Honor the LORD, all His people; those who
obey Him have all they need." (Ps 34:9)

Easter Weekday
Acts 5:17-26
Ps 34:2-9
Jn 3:16-21

St. Joseph the Worker
Gen 1:26—2:3 or Col 3:14-15,17,23-24
Ps 90:2,3-4,12-14,16
Mt 13:54-58

Thursday, May 2

ST. ATHANASIUS, BISHOP AND DOCTOR *(White)*

"We must obey God, not men." (Acts 5:29)

Acts 5:27-33
Ps 34:2,9,17-20
Jn 3:31-36

Friday, May 3

STS. PHILIP AND JAMES, APOSTLES *(Red)*

"You are saved by the gospel if you hold firmly to it..." (1 Cor 15:2b)

1 Cor 15:1-8
Ps 19:2-5
Jn 14:6-14

Saturday, May 4

EASTER WEEKDAY *(White)*
CANADA: BLESSED MARIE-LÉONIE PARADIS, VIRGIN *(White)*

"The words of the LORD are true, and all His works are dependable." (Ps 33:4)

Acts 6:1-7
Ps 33:1-2,4-5,18-19
Jn 6:16-21

A BALD EAGLE OVER KATMAI NATIONAL PARK, ALASKA

"In the Mass we find Bread and Wine for the soul. We find Love bending down to us, Love lifting us ever higher to Himself until all things are right and well with us."

from *Nazareth Family Spirituality*

Sunday, May 5

THIRD SUNDAY OF EASTER *(White)*

"[Jesus asked]... 'Do you love Me?'" (Jn 21:16)

Acts 5:27-32,40b-41
Ps 30:2,4-6,11-13
Rv 5:11-14
Jn 21:1-19

Monday, May 6

EASTER WEEKDAY *(White)*
CANADA: BLESSED FRANÇOIS DE-LAVAL, BISHOP *(White)*

"What God wants you to do is to believe in the
One He sent." (Jn 6:29)

Acts 6:8-15
Ps 119:23-24,26-27,29-30
Jn 6:22-29

Tuesday, May 7

EASTER WEEKDAY *(White)*

"Jesus told them. 'Those who come to Me will never
be hungry; those who believe in Me will never be
thirsty.'" (Jn 6:35)

Acts 7:51—8:1a
Ps 31:3-4,6-8,17,21
Jn 6:30-35

Wednesday, May 8

EASTER WEEKDAY *(White)*
CANADA: BLESSED CATHERINE DE ST. AUGUSTIN, VIRGIN *(White)*

"'I will never turn away anyone who comes to Me,' [Jesus said]... 'and I will raise them up on the last day.'" (Jn 6:37b,40b)

Acts 8:1b-8
Ps 66:1-7
Jn 6:35-40

Thursday, May 9

EASTER WEEKDAY *(White)*

"'I am the bread of life,' [Jesus said]... 'If you eat this bread, you will live forever.'" (Jn 6:48,51b)

Acts 8:26-40
Ps 66:8-9,16-17,20
Jn 6:44-51

Friday, May 10

EASTER WEEKDAY *(White)*
USA: BLESSED DAMIEN DE VEUSTER, PRIEST *(White)*

"Jesus said... 'Those who eat My flesh and drink My blood have eternal life, and I will raise them to life on the last day.'" (Jn 6:54)

Acts 9:1-20
Ps 117:1-2
Jn 6:52-59

Saturday, May 11

EASTER WEEKDAY *(White)*

"Lord, to whom [else] would we go? You have the words that give eternal life." (Jn 6:68)

Acts 9:31-42
Ps 116:12-17
Jn 6:60-69

KING PENGUINS ON SOUTH GEORGIA ISLAND

"What happened while [Mary] stood at the foot of the cross? Such a simple thing. Jesus turned to her and said that she is the mother of John and that John is her son. That made her the mother of the world: Protestants, Catholics, Moslems, Jews, Gentiles, pagans— all belong to her, all know her in one shape or another. She is the mother of all humankind."

from *Bogoroditza: She Who Gave Birth to God*

Sunday, May 12 <small>MOTHER'S DAY</small>

FOURTH SUNDAY OF EASTER *(White)*

"[Jesus said], 'I give [My sheep] eternal life...
No one can snatch them away from Me.'"
(Jn 10:28)

Acts 13:14,43-52
Ps 100:1-3,5
Rv 7:9,14b-17
Jn 10:27-30

Monday, May 13

EASTER WEEKDAY *(White)*; OUR LADY OF FATIMA *(White)*

"'...the sheep hear [the shepherd's] voice as he calls his own sheep by name...' [said the Good Shepherd]." (Jn 10:3b)

Acts 11:1-18
Ps 42:2-4; 43:3-4
Jn 10:1-10

Tuesday, May 14

ST. MATTHIAS, APOSTLE *(Red)*

"[Jesus told them], 'I love you just as the Father loves Me; remain in My love.'" (Jn 15:9)

Acts 1:15-17,20-26
Ps 113:1-8
Jn 15:9-17

Wednesday, May 15

EASTER WEEKDAY *(White)*
USA: ST. ISIDORE THE FARMER, HUSBAND *(White)*

"The words I [Jesus] have spoken will be
[people's] judge on the last day!" (Jn 12:48b)

Acts 12:24—13:5a
Ps 67:2-3,5-6,8
Jn 12:44-50

Thursday, May 16

EASTER WEEKDAY *(White)*

"No slaves are greater than their master, and no
messengers are greater than the one who sent
them." (Jn 13:16)

Acts 13:13-25
Ps 89:2-3,21-22,25,27
Jn 13:16-20

Friday, May 17

EASTER WEEKDAY (White)

"Jesus said, 'I am the way, the truth and the life.'" (Jn 14:6)

Acts 13:26-33
Ps 2:6-11
Jn 14:1-6

Saturday, May 18

EASTER WEEKDAY (White); ST. JOHN I, POPE AND MARTYR (Red)

"'Now that you have known Me,' [Jesus] said... 'you will know My Father also.'" (Jn 14:7)

Acts 13:44-52
Ps 98:1-4
Jn 14:7-14

A PIANO KEY BUTTERFLY IN SOUTHEASTERN FLORIDA

"Once you accept your own poverty before God, this truth will make you free to love and to serve."

from *Light in the Darkness: A Christian Vision for Unstable Times*

Sunday, May 19

FIFTH SUNDAY OF EASTER *(White)*

"Then I saw a new heaven and a new earth...
God will live with [His people]... There will be
no more death, no more grief or crying or pain."
(Rv 21:1,3c,4b)

Acts 14:21-27
Ps 145:8-13
Rv 21:1-5a
Jn 13:31-33a,34-35

Monday, May 20 <small>CANADA: VICTORIA DAY</small>

EASTER WEEKDAY *(White)*
ST. BERNARDINE OF SIENA, PRIEST *(White)*

"My Father will love those who love Me [Jesus];
I, too, will love them and reveal Myself to them."
(Jn 14:21b)

Acts 14:5-18
Ps 115:1-4,15-16
Jn 14:21-26

Tuesday, May 21

EASTER WEEKDAY *(White)*
ST. CHRISTOPHER MAGALLANES, PRIEST, AND COMPANIONS, MARTYRS *(Red)*
CANADA: ST. EUGÈNE DE MAZENOD, BISHOP *(White)*

"'[I]t is My own peace that I give you... Do not
be worried and upset; do not be afraid,' [Jesus
told them]." (Jn 14:27)

Acts 14:19-28
Ps 145:10-13,21
Jn 14:27-31a

Wednesday, May 22

EASTER WEEKDAY *(White)*
ST. RITA OF CASCIA, WIFE, MOTHER, RELIGIOUS *(White)*

"Those who remain in Me, and I in them, will bear much fruit; for you can do nothing without Me." (Jn 15:5)

Acts 15:1-6
Ps 122:2-5
Jn 15:1-8

Thursday, May 23

EASTER WEEKDAY *(White)*

"We believe and are saved by the grace of the Lord Jesus..." (Acts 15:11)

Acts 15:7-21
Ps 96:1-3,10
Jn 15:9-11

Friday, May 24

EASTER WEEKDAY *(White)*
CANADA: BLESSED LOUIS-ZÉPHIRIN MOREAU, BISHOP *(White)*

"[Jesus said], 'You did not choose Me; I chose you... to go and bear much fruit...'" (Jn 15:16)

Acts 15:22-31
Ps 57:8-12
Jn 15:12-17

Saturday, May 25

EASTER WEEKDAY *(White)*; ST. BEDE, PRIEST AND DOCTOR *(White)*
ST. GREGORY VII, POPE *(White)*
ST. MARY MAGDALENE DE'PAZZI, VIRGIN *(White)*

"'I chose you from this world,' [Jesus said], 'and you do not belong to it.'" (Jn 15:19)

Acts 16:1-10
Ps 100:1-3,5
Jn 15:18-21

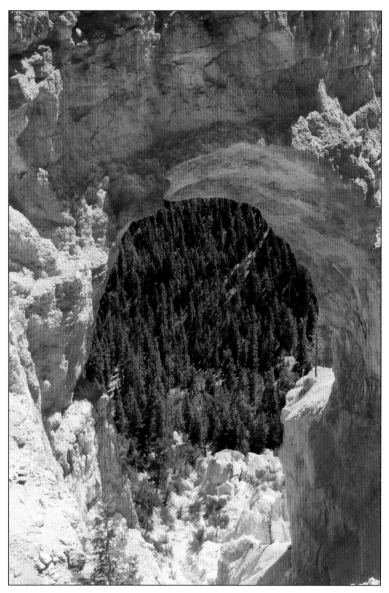

AN ARCH FORMATION IN BRYCE CANYON NATIONAL PARK, UTAH

"Is our love ever-watchful, ready to give to others the alms of gentle words? Our spoken words may be like a 'key' that can keep a door from closing. A gate may be opened, allowing light and love to flood minds that are beginning to doubt the very existence of love."

from *Donkey Bells: Christmas and Advent*

Sunday, May 26

SIXTH SUNDAY OF EASTER *(White)*

"Those who love Me will obey My teaching. My Father will love them, and My Father and I will come to them and live with them." (Jn 14:23)

Acts 15:1-2,22-29
Ps 67:2-3,5-6,8
Rv 21:10-14,22-23
Jn 14:23-29

Monday, May 27 MEMORIAL DAY

EASTER WEEKDAY *(White)*
ST. AUGUSTINE OF CANTERBURY, BISHOP *(White)*

"People will [persecute you] because they have
not known either the Father or Me [Jesus]."
(Jn 16:3)

Acts 16:11-15
Ps 149:1-6,9
Jn 15:26—16:4a

Tuesday, May 28

EASTER WEEKDAY *(White)*

"You answered me when I called to You, [LORD];
with Your strength You strengthened me."
(Ps 138:3)

Acts 16:22-34
Ps 138:1-3,7-8
Jn 16:5-11

Wednesday, May 29

EASTER WEEKDAY *(White)*

"Young women and young men, old people and children ...let them all praise the name of the LORD!" (Ps 148:12-13a)

Acts 17:15,22—18:1
Ps 148:1-2,11-14
Jn 16:12-15

Thursday, May 30   *HOLY DAY OF OBLIGATION*
(see appendix for where this applies)

THE ASCENSION OF THE LORD *(White)* (in some U.S. ecclesiastical provinces)
ELSEWHERE IN THE USA AND IN CANADA: EASTER WEEKDAY *(White)*

"'...I am going to the Father,' [Jesus told His disciples]." (Jn 16:17c)

ASCENSION:
Acts 1:1-11
Ps 47:2-3,6-9
Eph 1:17-23 or Heb 9:24-28; 10:19-23
Lk 24:46-53

EASTER WEEKDAY:
Acts 18:1-8
Ps 98:1-4
Jn 16:16-20

Friday, May 31

VISITATION OF THE BLESSED VIRGIN MARY *(White)*

"Ask God to bless those who persecute you—yes, ask Him to bless, not to curse." (Rom 12:14)

Zeph 3:14-18a or Rom 12:9-16
(Ps) Is 12:2-6
Lk 1:39-56

Saturday, June 1

ST. JUSTIN, MARTYR *(Red)*

"'...the Father Himself loves you,' [Jesus said], '...because you love Me...'" (Jn 16:27)

Acts 18:23-28
Ps 47:2-3,8-9,10
Jn 16:23b-28

THE WEST COAST OF CALIFORNIA

"The good that we do goes across the world and probably into the cosmos. The evil that we do follows the same path. It is rather fearsome, isn't it?"

from *In the Footprints of Loneliness: Meditations—when you hear an echo in your heart*

Sunday, June 2

THE ASCENSION OF THE LORD *(White)*
(in Canada and most U.S. ecclesiastical provinces)
ELSEWHERE IN USA: SEVENTH SUNDAY OF EASTER *(White)*

"[Jesus] said to [His disciples], 'This is what is written: the Messiah must suffer and must rise from death three days later, and in His name the message about repentance and the forgiveness of sins must be preached to all nations...' As He blessed them, He...was taken up into heaven." (Lk 24:46-47a,51)

Ascension:
Acts 1:1-11
Ps 47:2-3,6-9
Eph 1:17-23 or Heb 9:24-28; 10:19-23
Lk 24:46-53

Seventh Sunday of Easter:
Acts 7:55-60
Ps 97:1-2,6-7,9
Rv 22:12-14,16-17,20
Jn 17:20-26

Monday, June 3

ST. CHARLES LWANGA AND COMPANIONS, MARTYRS *(Red)*

"'The world will make you suffer,' [Jesus said].
'But be brave! I have defeated the world!'"
(Jn 16:33b)

Acts 19:1-8
Ps 68:2-7
Jn 16:29-33

Tuesday, June 4

EASTER WEEKDAY *(White)*

"Our God is a God who saves; He is the LORD,
our Lord, who rescues us from [eternal] death."
(Ps 68:20)

Acts 20:17-27
Ps 68:10-11,20-21
Jn 17:1-11a

Wednesday, June 5

ST. BONIFACE, BISHOP AND MARTYR *(Red)*

"I gave [My followers] Your message, [Father], and the world hated them, because they do not belong to the world, just as I [Jesus] do not belong to the world." (Jn 17:14)

Acts 20:28-38
Ps 68:29-30,33-36
Jn 17:11b-19

Thursday, June 6

EASTER WEEKDAY *(White)*; ST. NORBERT, BISHOP *(White)*

"[Jesus prayed to His Father]: 'I in them and You in Me, so that [those You gave Me] may be completely one, ...that the world may know that You sent Me and that You love them as You love Me." (Jn 17:23)

Acts 22:30; 23:6-11
Ps 16:1-2,5-11
Jn 17:20-26

Friday, June 7

EASTER WEEKDAY (White)

"As high as the sky is above the earth, so great is [God's] love for those who have reverence for Him." (Ps 103:11)

Acts 25:13b-21
Ps 103:1-2,11-12,19-20
Jn 21:15-19

Saturday, June 8

EASTER WEEKDAY (White)

"The Lord is righteous and loves good deeds; those who do them will live in His presence." (Ps 11:7)

Acts 28:16-20,30-31
Ps 11:4-5,7
Jn 21:20-25

A SUNSET IN MONTANA

"Oh Jesus, Son of God, I adore You with all my soul, my mind, my body. I pledge myself to Your service in whatever shape you want. ...With Your Holy Spirit at my side, I hope to be strong, even unto death."

from *On the Cross of Rejection: Meditations—when your heart is pierced*

Sunday, June 9

PENTECOST *(Red)*

"...by the Spirit's power we cry out to God, 'Father! my Father!' God's Spirit joins Himself to our spirits to declare that we are God's children." (Rom 8:15c-16)

Acts 2:1-11
Ps 104:1,24,29-31,34
1 Cor 12:3b-7,12-13 or Rom 8:8-17
Jn 20:19-23 or Jn 14:15-16,23b-26

Monday, June 10

WEEKDAY *(Green) - Tenth Week in Ordinary Time*

"Happy are those who know they are spiritually poor; the Kingdom of heaven belongs to them!" (Mt 5:3)

2 Cor 1:1-7
Ps 34:2-9
Mt 5:1-12

Tuesday, June 11

ST. BARNABAS, APOSTLE *(Red)*

"...your light must shine before people, so that they will see the good things you do and praise your Father in heaven." (Mt 5:16)

Acts 11:21b-26; 13:1-3
Ps 98:1-6
Mt 5:13-16

Wednesday, June 12

WEEKDAY *(Green)*

"The capacity we have [to do God's work] comes from God." (2 Cor 3:5b)

2 Cor 3:4-11
Ps 99:5-9
Mt 5:17-19

Thursday, June 13

ST. ANTHONY OF PADUA, PRIEST AND DOCTOR *(White)*

"God in His mercy has given us this work [of reflecting the glory of the Lord] to do, and so we do not become discouraged." (2 Cor 4:1)

2 Cor 3:15—4:1,3-6
Ps 85:9-14
Mt 5:20-26

Friday, June 14 <small>FLAG DAY</small>

<small>WEEKDAY *(Green)*</small>

"...anyone who looks at a woman and wants to possess her is guilty of committing adultery with her in his heart." (Mt 5:28)

2 Cor 4:7-15
Ps 116:10-11,15-18
Mt 5:27-32

Saturday, June 15

<small>WEEKDAY *(Green)*; BLESSED VIRGIN MARY *(White)*</small>

"...God...through Christ changed us from enemies into His friends and gave us the task of making others His friends also." (2 Cor 5:18)

2 Cor 5:14-21
Ps 103:1-4,8-9,11-12
Mt 5:33-37

A PRONGHORN ANTELOPE IN CUSTER STATE PARK, SOUTH DAKOTA

"If you are the father of a family, you cannot squander the money that should go for the education or 'whatever' of your children. There is a certain limit to what you can do in this situation, because that's your job, that's what God has called you to be: a protector, a provider. But, even if you can't give away your money, you can give *yourself*."

from *Donkey Bells: Christmas and Advent*

Sunday, June 16 FATHER'S DAY

THE MOST HOLY TRINITY *(White)*

"We...boast of our troubles, because we know that trouble produces endurance, endurance brings God's approval, and His approval brings hope. ... [F]or God has poured His love into our hearts through the Holy Spirit..." (Rom 5:3-4,5b)

Prv 8:22-31
Ps 8:4-9
Rom 5:1-5
Jn 16:12-15

Monday, June 17

WEEKDAY *(Green) - Eleventh Week in Ordinary Time*

"By our purity, knowledge, patience and kindness
we have shown ourselves to be God's servants—by
the Holy Spirit, by our true love, by our message
of truth, and by the power of God." (2 Cor 6:6-7a)

2 Cor 6:1-10
Ps 98:1-4
Mt 5:38-42

Tuesday, June 18

WEEKDAY *(Green)*

"Why should God reward you if you love only
the people who love you?" (Mt 5:46a)

2 Cor 8:1-9
Ps 146:2,5-9
Mt 5:43-48

Wednesday, June 19

WEEKDAY *(Green)*; ST. ROMUALD, ABBOT *(White)*

"Remember that the person who plants few seeds will have a small crop; the one who plants many seeds will have a large crop." (2 Cor 9:6)

2 Cor 9:6-11
Ps 112:1-4,9
Mt 6:1-6,16-18

Thursday, June 20

WEEKDAY *(Green)*

"Our Father in heaven...do not bring us to hard testing, but keep us safe from the Evil One." (Mt 6:9b,13)

2 Cor 11:1-11
Ps 111:1-4,7-8
Mt 6:7-15

Friday, June 21 *First Day of Summer*

ST. ALOYSIUS GONZAGA, RELIGIOUS *(White)*

"Store up riches for yourselves in heaven... For your heart will always be where your riches are." (Mt 6:20,21)

2 Cor 11:18,21-30
Ps 34:2-7
Mt 6:19-23

Saturday, June 22

WEEKDAY *(Green)*; ST. PAULINUS OF NOLA, BISHOP *(White)*
ST. JOHN FISHER, BISHOP AND MARTYR *(Red)*
ST. THOMAS MORE, HUSBAND, FATHER, MARTYR *(Red)*
BLESSED VIRGIN MARY *(White)*

"[The Lord said], 'My grace is all you need, for My power is greatest when you are weak.' I [Paul] am most happy, then, to be proud of my weaknesses..." (2 Cor 12:9ab)

2 Cor 12:1-10
Ps 34:8-13
Mt 6:24-34

A ROSE IN NORTHEASTERN ILLINOIS

"Love is not emotion and not a state. It is a Person—it is God Himself. He is the food I receive in the Eucharistic Sacrifice. I need Him daily because I am a sinner and weak. True, I am a saved sinner, but one who realizes only too well the words of Christ, 'Without Me you can do nothing' (Jn 15:5). I need Him, the Living Bread, to love through me."

from *Light in the Darkness: A Christian Vision for Unstable Times*

Sunday, June 23 CORPUS CHRISTI SUNDAY

THE MOST HOLY BODY AND BLOOD OF CHRIST *(White)*

"...the Lord Jesus...took a piece of bread, gave thanks to God, broke it and said, 'This is My body, which is for you. Do this in memory of Me.'"
(1 Cor 11:23b-24)

Gen 14:18-20
Ps 110:1-4
1 Cor 11:23-26
Lk 9:11b-17

Monday, June 24

THE NATIVITY OF ST. JOHN THE BAPTIST *(White)*

"You created every part of me, [O LORD]; You put me together in my mother's womb." (Ps 139:13)

Is 49:1-6
Ps 139:1-3,13-15
Acts 13:22-26
Lk 1:57-66,80

Tuesday, June 25

WEEKDAY *(Green)* - *Twelfth Week in Ordinary Time*

"Do for others what you want them to do for you." (Mt 7:12a)

Gen 13:2,5-18
Ps 15:2-5
Mt 7:6,12-14

Wednesday, June 26

WEEKDAY *(Green)*

"Be on your guard against false prophets; they come to you looking like sheep...but...they are really like wild wolves." (Mt 7:15)

Gen 15:1-12,17-18
Ps 105:1-4,6-9
Mt 7:15-20

Thursday, June 27

WEEKDAY *(Green)*
ST. CYRIL OF ALEXANDRIA, BISHOP AND DOCTOR *(White)*
CANADA: BLS. NYKYTA BUDKA AND VASYL VELYCHKOWSKY,
  BISHOPS AND MARTYRS *(Red)*

"[Jesus said], '...anyone who hears these words of Mine and obeys them is like a wise man who built his house on rock.'" (Mt 7:24)

Gen 16:1-12,15-16
Ps 106:1-5
Mt 7:21-29

Friday, June 28

THE MOST SACRED HEART OF JESUS *(White)*

"I [God] will look for those that are lost, bring back those that wander off, bandage those that are hurt, and heal those that are sick." (Ez 34:16)

Ez 34:11-16
Ps 23:1-6
Rom 5:5b-11
Lk 15:3-7

Saturday, June 29

STS. PETER AND PAUL, APOSTLES *(Red)*

"[Jesus said to Peter], 'I will give you the keys of the Kingdom of heaven; what you prohibit on earth will be prohibited in heaven, and what you permit on earth will be permitted in heaven.'" (Mt 16:19)

Acts 12:1-11
Ps 34:2-9
2 Tm 4:6-8,17-18
Mt 16:13-19

SPRINGBOKS AND AN ORYX IN NAMIBIA, AFRICA

"Lord, have mercy on us! Give us the grace to be at peace with You, with ourselves, and with our neighbors."

from *Grace in Every Season: Through the Year with Catherine Doherty*

Sunday, June 30

"Let love make you serve one another. For the whole Law is summed up in one commandment: 'Love your neighbor as you love yourself.'" (Gal 5:13c-14)

1 Kgs 19:16b,19-21
Ps 16:1-2,5,7-11
Gal 5:1,13-18
Lk 9:51-62

Monday, July 1 CANADA: CANADA DAY

WEEKDAY *(Green)*; USA: ST. JUNÍPERO SERRA, PRIEST *(White)*
CANADA: *RITUAL MASS FOR CANADA DAY (White)*

"As high as the sky is above the earth, so great is [the LORD's] love for those who honor Him." (Ps 103:11)

Gen 18:16-33
Ps 103:1-4,8-11
Mt 8:18-22

Tuesday, July 2

WEEKDAY *(Green)*

"Examine me and test me, LORD, judge my desires and thoughts." (Ps 26:2)

Gen 19:15-29
Ps 26:2-3,9-12
Mt 8:23-27

Wednesday, July 3

ST. THOMAS, APOSTLE *(Red)*

"Jesus...said, 'Peace be with you... Stop your
doubting and believe.'" (Jn 20:26,27)

Eph 2:19-22
Ps 117:1-2
Jn 20:24-29

Thursday, July 4   <small>USA: INDEPENDENCE DAY</small>

WEEKDAY *(Green); RITUAL MASS FOR INDEPENDENCE DAY (White)*
CANADA: ST. ELIZABETH OF PORTUGAL, WIFE, MOTHER, RELIGIOUS *(White)*

"To You alone, O Lord, to You alone, and not to
us, must glory be given..." (Ps 115:1)

Gen 22:1b-19
Ps 115:1-6,8-9
Mt 9:1-8

Friday, July 5

WEEKDAY *(Green)*; ST. ANTHONY ZACCARIA, PRIEST *(White)*
USA: ST. ELIZABETH OF PORTUGAL, WIFE, MOTHER, RELIGIOUS *(White)*

"Who can tell all the great things [the LORD] has done? Who can praise Him enough?" (Ps 106:2)

Gen 23:1-4,19; 24:1-8,62-67
Ps 106:1-5
Mt 9:9-13

Saturday, July 6

WEEKDAY *(Green)*; ST. MARIA GORETTI, VIRGIN AND MARTYR *(Red)*
BLESSED VIRGIN MARY *(White)*

"Praise the LORD! Praise His name, you servants of the LORD..." (Ps 135:1)

Gen 27:1-5,15-29
Ps 135:1-6
Mt 9:14-17

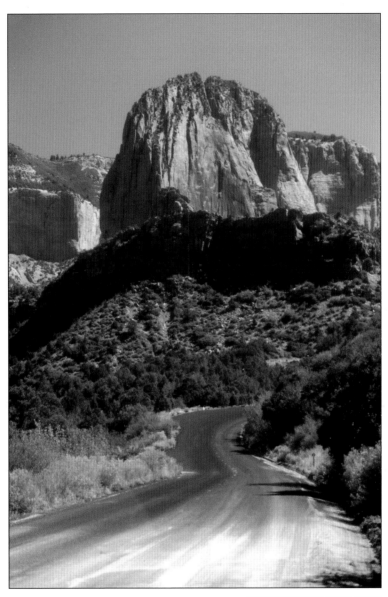

ZION NATIONAL PARK, UTAH

"Words are such wonderful things. Words console. Words strengthen. Our words can be like hands stretched out to our brothers and sisters, inviting them to walk the path of God."

from *Donkey Bells: Christmas and Advent*

Sunday, July 7

FOURTEENTH SUNDAY IN ORDINARY TIME *(Green)*

"...I will boast only about the cross of the Lord Jesus Christ; for by means of His cross the world is dead to me, and I am dead to the world." (Gal 6:14)

Is 66:10-14c
Ps 66:1-7,16,20
Gal 6:14-18
Lk 10:1-12,17-20

Monday, July 8

WEEKDAY *(Green)*

"Whoever goes to the LORD for safety...can say to Him, 'You are my defender and protector. You are my God; in You I trust.'" (Ps 91:1,2)

Gen 28:10-22a
Ps 91:1-4,14-15
Mt 9:18-26

Tuesday, July 9

WEEKDAY *(Green)*; ST. AUGUSTINE ZHAO RONG, PRIEST, AND HIS COMPANIONS, MARTYRS *(Red)*

"Pray to the owner of the harvest that He will send out workers to gather in His harvest." (Mt 9:38)

Gen 32:23-33
Ps 17:1-3,6-8,15
Mt 9:32-38

Wednesday, July 10

WEEKDAY *(Green)*

"The LORD watches over those who obey Him,
those who trust in His constant love." (Ps 33:18)

Gen 41:55-57; 42:5-7a,17-24a
Ps 33:2-3,10-11,18-19
Mt 10:1-7

Thursday, July 11

ST. BENEDICT, ABBOT *(White)*

"You received [from God] without paying, so
give without being paid." (Mt 10:8b)

Gen 44:18-21,23b-29; 45:1-5
Ps 105:16-21
Mt 10:7-15

Friday, July 12

WEEKDAY *(Green)*

"Seek your happiness in the LORD, and He will give you your heart's desire." (Ps 37:4)

Gen 46:1-7,28-30
Ps 37:3-4,18-19,27-28,39-40
Mt 10:16-23

Saturday, July 13

WEEKDAY *(Green)*; ST. HENRY, EMPEROR, HUSBAND, FATHER *(White)*
BLESSED VIRGIN MARY *(White)*

"...not one sparrow falls to the ground without your Father's consent... So do not be afraid; you are worth much more than many sparrows!" (Mt 10:29,31)

Gen 49:29-32; 50:15-26a
Ps 105:1-4,6-7
Mt 10:24-33

A RED FOX NEAR SANDSTONE, MINNESOTA

"At Madonna House we paint these words unto all our mirrors, 'God's image,' so that when anyone looks in the mirror, they see that they are God's image. I think the greatest work that we have to do in this civilization, this country, is to accept ourselves as lovable."

from *Nazareth Family Spirituality*

Sunday, July 14

FIFTEENTH SUNDAY IN ORDINARY TIME *(Green)*

"Jesus [asked], '...which one...acted like a neighbor?' ...The teacher of the Law answered, 'The one who was kind...' Jesus replied, 'You go, then, and do the same.'" (Lk 10:36-37)

Dt 30:10-14
Ps 69:14,17,30-31,33-34,36-37
Col 1:15-20
Lk 10:25-37

Monday, July 15

ST. BONAVENTURE, BISHOP AND DOCTOR *(White)*

"You can be sure that whoever gives even a drink of cold water to one of the least of...My [Jesus'] followers because he is My follower, will...receive a reward." (Mt 10:42)

Ex 1:8-14,22
Ps 124:1-8
Mt 10:34—11:1

Tuesday, July 16

WEEKDAY *(Green)*
OUR LADY OF MOUNT CARMEL *(White)*

"I will praise God with a song; I will proclaim His greatness by giving Him thanks." (Ps 69:30)

Ex 2:1-15a
Ps 69:3,14,30-31,33-34
Mt 11:20-24

Wednesday, July 17

WEEKDAY *(Green)*

"Father, Lord of heaven and earth! I thank You because You have shown to the unlearned what You have hidden from the wise and the learned." (Mt 11:25)

Ex 3:1-6,9-12
Ps 103:1-4,6-7
Mt 11:25-27

Thursday, July 18

WEEKDAY *(Green)*
USA: ST. CAMILLUS DE LELLIS, PRIEST *(White)*

"'Take My yoke and put it on you,' [Jesus said], 'and learn from Me... I am gentle and humble in spirit; and you will find rest.'" (Mt 11:29)

Ex 3:13-20
Ps 105:1,5,8-9,24-27
Mt 11:28-30

Friday, July 19

WEEKDAY *(Green)*

"I am Your servant, LORD." (Ps 116:16a)

Ex 11:10—12:14
Ps 116:12-13,15-18
Mt 12:1-8

Saturday, July 20

WEEKDAY *(Green)*; ST. APOLLINARIUS, BISHOP AND MARTYR *(Red)*
BLESSED VIRGIN MARY *(White)*

"[The LORD] did not forget us when we were defeated; His love is eternal." (Ps 136:23)

Ex 12:37-42
Ps 136:1,10-15,23-24
Mt 12:14-21

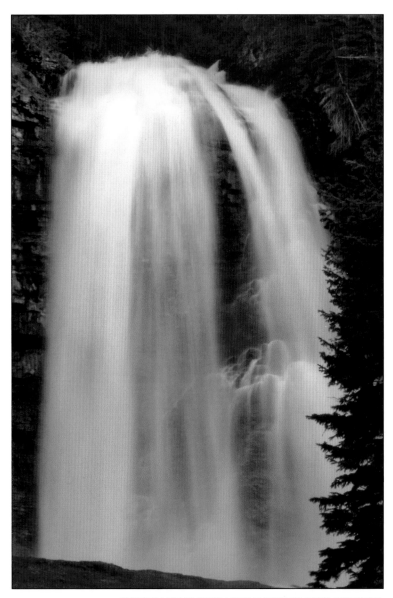

VIRGINIA FALLS IN GLACIER NATIONAL PARK, MONTANA

"To be before God means to remember who God is. To render Him, therefore, the adoration and love that are His due from us, His creatures. It means remembering our last end and fulfilling the obligations of a prayer-life that will lead us there. It means knowing that we are an empty cup that daily must be filled by God, and going to Him to have the cup filled."

from *Grace in Every Season: Through the Year with Catherine Doherty*

Sunday, July 21

SIXTEENTH SUNDAY IN ORDINARY TIME *(Green)*

"I am happy about my sufferings...for by means of [them] I am helping to complete what still remains of Christ's sufferings on behalf of His body, the church." (Col 1:24)

Gen 18:1-10a
Ps 15:2-5
Col 1:24-28
Lk 10:38-42

Monday, July 22

ST. MARY MAGDALENE, DISCIPLE OF THE LORD *(White)*

"Anyone who is joined to Christ is a new being;
the old is gone, the new has come." (2 Cor 5:17)

Sg 3:1-4b or 2 Cor 5:14-17
Ps 63:2-6,8-9
Jn 20:1-2,11-18

Tuesday, July 23

WEEKDAY *(Green)*
ST. BRIDGET OF SWEDEN, WIFE, MOTHER, RELIGIOUS *(White)*

"[Jesus said], 'Whoever does what My Father
in heaven wants is My brother, My sister, and
My mother.'" (Mt 12:50)

Ex 14:21—15:1
(Ps) Ex 15:8-10,12,17
Mt 12:46-50

Wednesday, July 24

WEEKDAY *(Green)*
ST. SHARBEL MAKHLUF, PRIEST *(White)*

"Listen [to the word of God] if you have ears!"
(Mt 13:9)

Ex 16:1-5,9-15
Ps 78:18-19,23-28
Mt 13:1-9

Thursday, July 25

ST. JAMES, APOSTLE *(Red)*

"We who have [Christ] are like common clay
pots, in order to show that the supreme power
belongs to God, not to us." (2 Cor 4:7)

2 Cor 4:7-15
Ps 126: 1-6
Mt 20:20-28

Friday, July 26

STS. JOACHIM AND ANNE, PARENTS OF THE BLESSED VIRGIN MARY *(White)*
St. Anne is the Patron of the Province of Quebec

"The commands of the LORD are just and give understanding to the mind." (Ps 19:8b)

Ex 20:1-17
Ps 19:8-11
Mt 13:18-23

Saturday, July 27

WEEKDAY *(Green)*; BLESSED VIRGIN MARY *(White)*

"Let the giving of thanks be your sacrifice to God..." (Ps 50:14a)

Ex 24:3-8
Ps 50:1-2,5-6,14-15
Mt 13:24-30

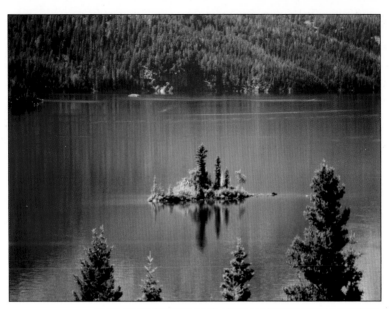

WILD GOOSE ISLAND IN GLACIER NATIONAL PARK, MONTANA

"Let us stop for a moment—forget the mad pursuit of a security that is not to be found on earth—forget the driving urge for perishable goods—forget, above all, *ourselves*. Let us begin to think of God, and of the quality of mercy that will bring us face to face with Him tomorrow and give peace to our hectic days."

from *Grace in Every Season: Through the Year with Catherine Doherty*

Sunday, July 28

SEVENTEENTH SUNDAY IN ORDINARY TIME *(Green)*

"Those who ask will receive, those who seek will find, and the door will be opened to anyone who knocks." (Lk 11:10)

Gen 18:20-32
Ps 138:1-3,6-8
Col 2:12-14
Lk 11:1-13

Monday, July 29

ST. MARTHA, DISCIPLE OF THE LORD *(White)*

"[Jesus said]... 'whoever lives and believes in Me will never die. Do you believe this?'" (Jn 11:26)

Ex 32:15-24,30-34
Ps 106:19-23
Jn 11:19-27 or Lk 10:38-42

Tuesday, July 30

WEEKDAY *(Green)*
ST. PETER CHRYSOLOGUS, BISHOP AND DOCTOR *(White)*
BL. SOLANUS CASEY, PRIEST *(White)*

"God's people will shine like the sun in their Father's Kingdom." (Mt 13:43a)

Ex 33:7-11; 34:5b-9,28
Ps 103:6-13
Mt 13:36-43

Wednesday, July 31

ST. IGNATIUS OF LOYOLA, PRIEST *(White)*

"Praise the LORD our God... Holy is He!"
(Ps 99:5)

Ex 34:29-35
Ps 99:5-7,9
Mt 13:44-46

Thursday, August 1

ST. ALPHONSUS LIGUORI, BISHOP AND DOCTOR *(White)*

"The LORD is our protector and glorious king,
blessing us with kindness and honor." (Ps 84:11)

Ex 40:16-21,34-38
Ps 84:3-6,8,11
Mt 13:47-53

Friday, August 2

WEEKDAY *(Green)*; ST. EUSEBIUS OF VERCELLI, BISHOP *(White)*
ST. PETER JULIAN EYMARD, PRIEST *(White)*

"I am the LORD your God... Open your mouth
and I will feed you." (Ps 81:10)

Lv 23:1,4-11,15-16,27,34b-37
Ps 81:3-6,10-11
Mt 13:54-58

Saturday, August 3

WEEKDAY *(Green)*; BLESSED VIRGIN MARY *(White)*

"Do not cheat [others], but obey the LORD your
God." (Lv 25:17)

Lv 25:1,8-17
Ps 67:2-3,5,7-8
Mt 14:1-12

THE SKY OVER DEATH VALLEY, CALIFORNIA

"Beloved, I feel like the apostles, 'Lord, it is good for us to be here.' At Your feet, I rest in a peace that transcends word and passes understanding. In that peace, thoughts come to me that do not otherwise appear. I see the world torn away from You. I see the cause of its misery in having denied, rejected Your existence, yet yearning for You as never before."

from *On the Cross of Rejection: Meditations — when your heart is pierced*

Sunday, August 4

EIGHTEENTH SUNDAY IN ORDINARY TIME *(Green)*

"Watch out and guard yourselves from every kind of greed; because your true life is not made up of the things you own, no matter how rich you may be." (Lk 12:15)

Eccl 1:2; 2:21-23
Ps 95:1-2,6-9
Col 3:1-5,9-11
Lk 12:13-21

Monday, August 5

WEEKDAY *(Green)*; DEDICATION OF THE ST. MARY MAJOR BASILICA *(White)*
CANADA: BLESSED FRÉDÉRIC JANSSOONE, PRIEST *(White)*

"[The LORD says]... 'How I wish My people would
listen to Me; how I wish they would obey Me!"
(Ps 81:13)

Num 11:4b-15
Ps 81:12-17
Mt 14:13-21

Tuesday, August 6

TRANSFIGURATION OF THE LORD *(White)*

"[God's] voice said from the cloud, 'This is My
Son, whom I have chosen—listen to Him.'"
(Lk 9:35)

Dan 7:9-10,13-14
Ps 97:1-2,5-6,9
2 Pt 1:16-19
Lk 9:28b-36

Wednesday, August 7

WEEKDAY *(Green)*; ST. SIXTUS II, POPE AND COMPANIONS, MARTYRS *(Red)*
ST. CAJETAN, PRIEST *(White)*

"We have sinned as our ancestors did... They forgot the many times [God] showed them His love..." (Ps 106:6a,7b)

Num 13:1-2,25—14:1,26-29a,34-35
Ps 106:6-7,13-14,21-23
Mt 15:21-28

Thursday, August 8

ST. DOMINIC, PRIEST *(White)*

"'What about you?' [Jesus] asked... 'Who do you say I am?'" (Mt 16:15)

Num 20:1-13
Ps 95:1-2,6-9
Mt 16:13-23

Friday, August 9

WEEKDAY *(Green)*
ST. TERESA BENEDICTA OF THE CROSS, VIRGIN AND MARTYR *(Red)*

"Will a person gain anything if he wins the whole world but loses his [eternal] life?" (Mt 16:26a)

Dt 4:32-40
Ps 77:12-16,21
Mt 16:24-28

Saturday, August 10

ST. LAWRENCE, DEACON AND MARTYR *(Red)*

"'My Father will honor anyone who serves Me,' [Jesus said]." (Jn 12:26b)

2 Cor 9:6-10
Ps 112:1-2,5-9
Jn 12:24-26

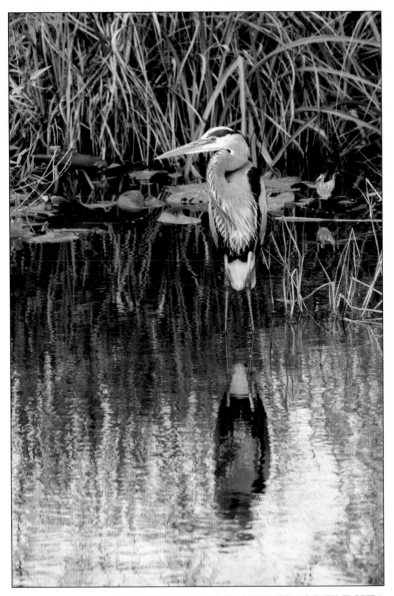

A BLUE HERON IN EVERGLADES NATIONAL PARK, FLORIDA

"O Beloved, how peaceful You are! How quiet! How tranquil! How strong! The voices of the world die into silence at the threshold of a soul filled with You. Give me Your peace. I love You, teach me Your holy, quiet strength! Beloved, I love You!"

from *O Jesus: Prayers from the Diaries of Catherine DeHueck Doherty*

Sunday, August 11

NINETEENTH SUNDAY IN ORDINARY TIME *(Green)*

"Do not be afraid, little flock, for your Father is pleased to give you the Kingdom... [So] save your riches in heaven... For your heart will always be where your riches are." (Lk 12:32,33c,34)

Wis 18:6-9
Ps 33:1,12,18-22
Heb 11:1-2,8-19
Lk 12:32-48

Monday, August 12

WEEKDAY *(Green)*
ST. JANE FRANCES DE CHANTAL, WIFE, MOTHER, RELIGIOUS *(White)*

"Have reverence for the LORD your God and worship only Him." (Dt 10:20a)

Dt 10:12-22
Ps 147:12-15,19-20
Mt 17:22-27

Tuesday, August 13

WEEKDAY *(Green)*
STS PONTIAN, POPE, AND HIPPOLYTUS, PRIEST, MARTYRS *(Red)*

"[Jesus said], 'The greatest in the Kingdom of heaven is the one who humbles himself and becomes like [a] child.'" (Mt 18:4)

Dt 31:1-8
Ps 32:3-4,7-9,12
Mt 18:1-5,10,12-14

Wednesday, August 14

ST. MAXIMILIAN KOLBE, PRIEST AND MARTYR *(Red)*

"If your brother sins against you, go to him and show him his fault. But do it privately, just between yourselves." (Mt 18:15)

Dt 34:1-12
Ps 66:1-3,5,8,16-17
Mt 18:15-20

Thursday, August 15   *HOLY DAY OF OBLIGATION*

THE ASSUMPTION OF THE BLESSED VIRGIN MARY *(White)*

"You, [Mary], are most blessed of all women." (Lk 1:42)

Rv 11:19a; 12:1-6a,10ab
Ps 45:10-12,16
1 Cor 15:20-27
Lk 1:39-56

Friday, August 16

WEEKDAY *(Green)*
ST. STEPHEN OF HUNGARY, HUSBAND, FATHER, KING *(White)*

"[Jesus said], '...a man will...unite with his wife, and the two will become one... No human being must separate, then, what God has joined together.'" (Mt 19:5-6)

Jos 24:1-13
Ps 136:1-3,16-18,21-22,24
Mt 19:3-12

Saturday, August 17

WEEKDAY *(Green)*; BLESSED VIRGIN MARY *(White)*

"...decide today whom you will serve... As for my family and me, we will serve the LORD." (Jos 24:15a,d)

Jos 24:14-29
Ps 16:1-2,5,7-8,11
Mt 19:13-15

MAMMOTH HOT SPRINGS IN YELLOWSTONE NATIONAL PARK, WYOMING

"The greatest tragedy in the world is mortal sin. Yet how few of us realize it. To sin is to die. To sin is to be empty. Mortal sin, which is not spoken of today, is an offense against God."

from *Beginning Again: Recovering Your Innocence and Joy through Confession*

Sunday, August 18

TWENTIETH SUNDAY IN ORDINARY TIME *(Green)*

"Let us keep our eyes fixed on Jesus, on whom
our faith depends from beginning to end."
(Heb 12:2a)

Jer 38:4-6,8-10
Ps 40:2-4,18
Heb 12:1-4
Lk 12:49-53

Monday, August 19

WEEKDAY *(Green)*
ST. JOHN EUDES, PRIEST *(White)*

"Keep the commandments if you want to enter life." (Mt 19:17b)

Jgs 2:11-19
Ps 106:34-37,39-40,43,44
Mt 19:16-22

Tuesday, August 20

ST. BERNARD, ABBOT AND DOCTOR *(White)*

"[Jesus said], '...everyone who leaves [family] or fields for My sake will receive a hundred times more and will be given eternal life.'" (Mt 19:29)

Jgs 6:11-24a
Ps 85:9,11-14
Mt 19:23-30

Wednesday, August 21

ST. PIUS X, POPE (White)

"Jesus concluded, 'So those who are last will
be first, and those who are first will be last.'"
(Mt 20:16)

Jgs 9:6-15
Ps 21:2-7
Mt 20:1-16

Thursday, August 22

QUEENSHIP OF THE BLESSED VIRGIN MARY (White)

"How I love to do Your will, my God! I keep
Your teaching in my heart." (Ps 40:8)

Jgs 11:29-39a
Ps 40:5,7-10
Mt 22:1-14

Friday, August 23

WEEKDAY *(Green)*
ST. ROSE OF LIMA, VIRGIN *(White)*

"Love the Lord your God with all your heart...
soul and...mind... Love your neighbor as you
love yourself." (Mt 22:37,39)

Ru 1:1,3-6,14b-16,22
Ps 146:5-10
Mt 22:34-40

Saturday, August 24

ST. BARTHOLOMEW, APOSTLE *(Red)*

"All Your creatures, LORD, will praise You, and all
Your people will give You thanks." (Ps 145:10)

Rv 21:9b-14
Ps 145:10-13,17-18
Jn 1:45-51

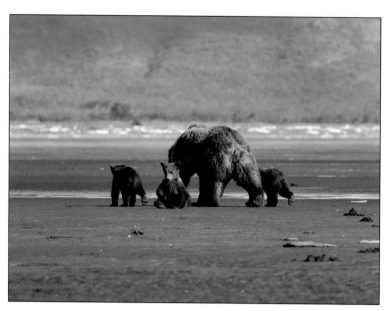

BROWN BEAR SOW AND CUBS IN KATMAI NATIONAL PARK, ALASKA

"Sin means forgetting God. It's a separation from Him, a turning of our backs to Him, sin is my rejection of God. I simply say to God, 'Look, I am tired of Your commandments, and what you eternally ask of me in the name of love. I want to do what I want to do when I want to do it, and I don't want You to dictate anything to me.'"

from *Kiss of Christ: Reflections on the Sacrament of Penance and Reconciliation*

Sunday, August 25

TWENTY-FIRST SUNDAY IN ORDINARY TIME *(Green)*

"...in the Kingdom of God...those who are now last will be first, and those who are now first will be last." (Lk 13:30)

Is 66:18-21
Ps 117:1-2
Heb 12:5-7,11-13
Lk 13:22-30

Monday, August 26

WEEKDAY *(Green)*

"Our friends, we know that God loves you and has chosen you to be His own." (1 Thes 1:4)

1 Thes 1:1-5,8b-10
Ps 149:1-6,9
Mt 23:13-22

Tuesday, August 27

ST. MONICA, WIFE AND MOTHER *(White)*

"We do not try to please people, but to please God, who tests our motives." (1 Thes 2:4c)

1 Thes 2:1-8
Ps 139:1-6
Mt 23:23-26

Wednesday, August 28

ST. AUGUSTINE, BISHOP AND DOCTOR *(White)*

"God is at work in you who believe."
(1 Thes 2:13c)

1 Thes 2:9-13
Ps 139:7-12
Mt 23:27-32

Thursday, August 29

THE PASSION OF ST. JOHN THE BAPTIST *(Red)*

"[The Lord] will strengthen you [in loving], and
you will be perfect and holy in the presence of
our God and Father when our Lord Jesus
comes..." (1 Thes 3:13)

1 Thes 3:7-13
Ps 90:3-4,12-14,17
Mk 6:17-29

Friday, August 30

WEEKDAY *(Green)*

"God did not call us to live in immorality, but in holiness. So then, whoever rejects this teaching is not rejecting a human being but God..." (1 Thes 4:7-8)

1 Thes 4:1-8
Ps 97:1-2,5-6,10-12
Mt 25:1-13

Saturday, August 31

WEEKDAY *(Green)*; BLESSED VIRGIN MARY *(White)*

"Make it your aim to live a quiet life, to mind your own business, and to earn your own living..." (1 Thes 4:11)

1 Thes 4:9-11
Ps 98:1,7-9
Mt 25:14-30

A WOOD STORK IN EVERGLADES NATIONAL PARK, FLORIDA

"God has given this day into our hands. This is the day in which we pray, but we pray by action and sweat, just as Christ did. He said He came 'not to be served but to serve' (Mt 20:28). He also said, 'Pray continually' (Lk 18:1). Pray while you work and work while you pray."

from *Living the Gospel without Compromise*

Sunday, September 1

TWENTY-SECOND SUNDAY IN ORDINARY TIME *(Green)*

"When you give a feast, invite the poor, the crippled, the lame and the blind; and you will be blessed, because they are not able to pay you back. God will repay you on the day the good people rise from death." (Lk 14:13-14)

Sir 3:17-18,20,28-29
Ps 68:4-7,10-11
Heb 12:18-19,22-24a
Lk 14:1,7-14

Monday, September 2 USA and CANADA: LABOR DAY

WEEKDAY *(Green)*
CANADA: BL. ANDRÉ GRASSET, PRIEST AND MARTYR *(Red)*

"...we believe that God will take back with Jesus
those who have died believing in Him."
(1 Thes 4:14b)

Weekday:
1 Thes 4:13-18
Ps 96:1,3-5,11-13
Lk 4:16-30

Labor Day USA:
Gen 1:26—2:3 or Gen 2:4-9,15
Ps 90:2-4,12-14,16 or Ps 127:1-2
2 Thes 3:6-12,16
Mt 6:31-34 or Mt 25:14-30

Tuesday, September 3

ST. GREGORY THE GREAT, POPE AND DOCTOR *(White)*

"The LORD is my light and my salvation; I will
fear no one." (Ps 27:1a)

1 Thes 5:1-6,9-11
Ps 27:1,4,13-14
Lk 4:31-37

Wednesday, September 4

WEEKDAY *(Green)*
CANADA: BLESSED DINA BÉLANGER, VIRGIN *(White)*

"The gospel keeps bringing blessings and is spreading throughout the world..." (Col 1:6)

Col 1:1-8
Ps 52:10-11
Lk 4:38-44

Thursday, September 5

WEEKDAY *(Green)*

"We ask God to fill you with the knowledge of His will, with all the wisdom and understanding that His Spirit gives...[so] your lives will produce all kinds of good deeds..." (Col 1:9b,10b)

Col 1:9-14
Ps 98:2-6
Lk 5:1-11

Friday, September 6

WEEKDAY *(Green)*

"[Christ] is the head of His body, the church; He is the source of the body's life." (Col 1:18a)

Col 1:15-20
Ps 100:1-5
Lk 5:33-39

Saturday, September 7

WEEKDAY *(Green)*; BLESSED VIRGIN MARY *(White)*

"I will gladly offer You a sacrifice, O LORD, I will give You thanks because You are good." (Ps 54:6)

Col 1:21-23
Ps 54:3-4,6,8
Lk 6:1-5

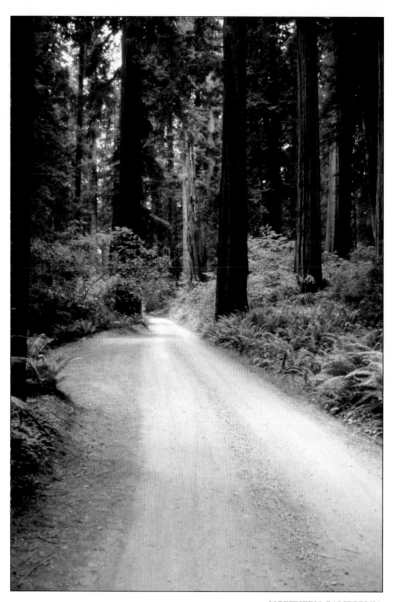

NORTHERN CALIFORNIA

"The weight of listening is heavy. [So] we need to pray for [the Lord] to make straight [His] ways...in our hearts. Then God...might walk these paths unencumbered. He can come into our hearts and ... listen ... talk ... understand ... help ... [and] console [through us] those who come to us... [W]hat better service could there be than to have a listening ear of God in our hearts?"

from *Grace in Every Season: Through the Year with Catherine Doherty*

Sunday, September 8

TWENTY-THIRD SUNDAY IN ORDINARY TIME *(Green)*

"Those who come to Me cannot be My disciples unless they love Me more than they love father and mother, wife and children, brothers and sisters, and themselves as well." (Lk 14:26)

Wis 9:13-18b
Ps 90:3-6,12-17
Phlm 9-10,12-17
Lk 14:25-33

Monday, September 9

ST. PETER CLAVER, PRIEST *(White)*

"...Christ is in you, which means that you will share in the glory of God." (Col 1:27b)

Col 1:24—2:3
Ps 62:6-7,9
Lk 6:6-11

Tuesday, September 10

WEEKDAY *(Green)*

"Keep your roots deep in [Christ Jesus], build your lives on Him... become stronger in your faith...and be filled with thanksgiving." (Col 2:7)

Col 2:6-15
Ps 145:1-2,8-11
Lk 6:12-19

Wednesday, September 11

WEEKDAY *(Green)*

"Now you must get rid of...anger, passion and hateful feelings. No insults or obscene talk must ever come from your lips." (Col 3:8)

Col 3:1-11
Ps 145:2-3,10-13
Lk 6:20-26

Thursday, September 12

WEEKDAY *(Green)*
THE MOST HOLY NAME OF MARY *(White)*

"You are the people of God; He loved you and chose you as His own... [So you] must forgive one another just as the Lord has forgiven you." (Col 3:12,13c)

Col 3:12-17
Ps 150:1-6
Lk 6:27-38

Friday, September 13

ST. JOHN CHRYSOSTOM, BISHOP AND DOCTOR *(White)*

"May God the Father and Christ Jesus our Lord give you grace, mercy and peace." (1 Tm 2b)

1 Tm 1:1-2,12-14
Ps 16:1-2,5,7-8,11
Lk 6:39-42

Saturday, September 14

EXALTATION OF THE HOLY CROSS *(Red)*

"...God did not send His Son into the world to be its judge, but to be its savior." (Jn 3:17)

Num 21:4b-9
Ps 78:1-2,34-38
Phil 2:6-11
Jn 3:13-17

WOOD STORKS IN THE WAKODAHATCHEE WETLANDS, FLORIDA

"Marriage is the most glorious adventure which a man and a woman can undertake, provided its basis is love, not lust. Love is in the heart, not in bodily functions. If we are in love with God, we will not spoil His image in ourselves or in others. Sex is a precious gift and is not to be treated lightly."

from *God in the Nitty Gritty Life*

Sunday, September 15

TWENTY-FOURTH SUNDAY IN ORDINARY TIME *(Green)*

"This man [Jesus] welcomes outcasts and even eats with them!" (Lk 15:2)

Ex 32:7-11,13-14
Ps 51:3-4,12-13,17,19
1 Tm 1:12-17
Lk 15:1-32

ORDER FORM

To order copies of *Listen to the Spirit—He Will Lead You 2020 Prayer Journal*, please use the order blank printed below.

TRINITY PHOTOGRAPHY
3805 7th St. NE #109
Great Falls, MT 59404-1154
<u>OR</u>

PHONE orders: **1-888-220-5941** (toll free)
E-MAIL orders: **catholicprayerdiary@gmail.com**
ONLINE orders: **www.catholicprayerdiary.com**

COST in U.S. DOLLARS

<u>U.S.A.</u>   **1 - 5** journals . . . . **$16.99** each
                 6 - 9 journals . . . . **$15.99** each
                 10 or more journals . . .**$14.99** each

***** *WE <u>PAY</u> <u>THE</u> <u>SHIPPING</u> within the <u>U.S.!!!</u>* *****

<u>CANADA</u>   Contact: **Madonna House Publications**,
                 2888 Dafoe Rd., RR #2, Combermere, Ontario K0J 1L0
                 1-888-703-7110 (toll free)
                 publications@madonnahouse.org
*<u>**Madonna House has its own pricing and shipping policies.**</u>***

I order _____ journal(s) at _____ each. *TOTAL: $*_____

Method of Payment: ___ **Check**   ___ **Money Order**   ___ **Discover**

___**Visa** ___**Mastercard - Card**#_____

Expires _____ **Security #s**_____ **Sign**_____
             (3 digits on back of card)   (as your name appears on your card)

(Please <u>PRINT</u>)

Send to _____

Address _____

_____

City_____State_____

Zip Code_____Phone _____
                         (required for credit card purchases)

(Allow 2-3 weeks for delivery)
THANK YOU FOR YOUR ORDER!

TO ORDER PHOTOGRAPHS

If you would like to order prints of any of the photographs included in this calendar, or to inquire about obtaining permission to use any of them in your own publication, please contact Trinity Photography contact person, Sandy Wedel, to discuss size, finish, and other specifications, as well as to obtain prices.

Write: **ATTN: Sandy Wedel**
Trinity Photography
3805 7th St. NE #109
Great Falls, MT 59404-1154

Phone: **1-888-220-5941**

E-Mail: **catholicprayerdiary@gmail.com**

Please include **your name** and **phone number** in any type of correspondence.

Monday, September 16

STS. CORNELIUS, POPE AND CYPRIAN, BISHOP, MARTYRS *(Red)*

"God our Savior...wants everyone to be saved and to come to know the truth." (1 Tm 2:4)

1 Tim 2:1-8
Ps 28:2,7-9
Lk 7:1-10

Tuesday, September 17

WEEKDAY *(Green)*
ST. ROBERT BELLARMINE, BISHOP AND DOCTOR *(White)*

"[Church helpers] should hold to the revealed truth of the faith with a clear conscience." (1 Tm 3:9)

1 Tm 3:1-13
Ps 101:1-3,5-6
Lk 7:11-17

Wednesday, September 18

WEEKDAY *(Green)*

"...the church of the living God [is] the pillar and support of the truth." (1 Tm 3:15)

1 Tm 3:14-16
Ps 111:1-6
Lk 7:31-35

Thursday, September 19

WEEKDAY *(Green)*
ST. JANUARIUS, BISHOP AND MARTYR *(Red)*

"The way to become wise is to honor the LORD; He gives sound judgment to all who obey His commands." (Ps 111:10)

1 Tm 4:12-16
Ps 111:7-10
Lk 7:36-50

Friday, September 20

STS. ANDREW KIM TAEGON, PRIEST AND MARTYR, AND
PAUL CHONG HASANG AND COMPANIONS, MARTYRS *(Red)*

"Whoever teaches a different doctrine and does
not agree with the true words of our Lord...is
swollen with pride and knows nothing."
(1 Tm 6:3-4)

1 Tim 6:2c-12
Ps 49:6-10,17-20
Lk 8:1-3

Saturday, September 21

ST. MATTHEW, APOSTLE AND EVANGELIST *(Red)*

"Live a life that measures up to the standard
God set when He called you. Be always humble,
gentle and patient." (Eph 4:1b-2a)

Eph 4:1-7,11-13
Ps 19:2-5
Mt 9:9-13

GLACIER NATIONAL PARK, MONTANA

"You are *God* and I am a *sinner*, but I am a sinner, a pauper, a person, a weak one *who loves*. If I truly love and strive to love with an ever-growing fire, then You can and will pass through me."

from *On the Cross of Rejection: Meditations—when your heart is pierced*

Sunday, September 22

TWENTY-FIFTH SUNDAY IN ORDINARY TIME *(Green)*

"I urge that petitions, prayers, requests, and thanksgivings be offered to God for all people... This is good and...pleases God our Savior, who wants everyone to be saved and to come to know the truth." (1 Tm 2:1,3-4)

Am 8:4-7
Ps 113:1-2,4-8
1 Tm 2:1-8
Lk 16:1-13

Monday, September 23 *First Day of Autumn*

ST. PIO OF PIETRELCINA, PRIEST *(White)*
CANADA: BLESSED EMILIE TAVERNIER-GAMELIN,
   WIFE, MOTHER, RELIGIOUS *(White)*

"No one lights a lamp and covers it... Instead it is put on the lampstand, so that people will see the light..." (Lk 8:16)

Ezr 1:1-6
Ps 126:1-6
Lk 8:16-18

Tuesday, September 24

WEEKDAY *(Green)*

"Jesus said, 'My mother and brothers are those who hear the word of God and obey it.'" (Lk 8:21)

Ezr 6:7-8,12b,14-20
Ps 122:1-5
Lk 8:19-21

Wednesday, September 25

WEEKDAY *(Green)*
CANADA: STS. COSMAS AND DAMIAN, MARTYRS *(Red)*

"Remember what God has done for you, and give thanks with all your heart." (Tob 13:6b)

Ezr 9:5-9
(Ps) Tob 13:2-4,6-8
Lk 9:1-6

Thursday, September 26

WEEKDAY *(Green)*; USA: STS. COSMAS AND DAMIAN, MARTYRS *(Red)*
CANADA: STS. JEAN DE BRÉBEUF, ISAAC JOGUES, PRIESTS,
    AND COMPANIONS, MARTYRS; *(Red) (Secondary Patrons of Canada)*

"The LORD takes pleasure in His people..." (Ps 149:4a)

Hag 1:1-8
Ps 149:1-6,9
Lk 9:7-9

Friday, September 27

ST. VINCENT DE PAUL, PRIEST *(White)*

"'...I promised that I would always be with you. I am still with you, so do not be afraid,' [says the LORD]." (Hag 2:5)

Hag 2:1-9
Ps 43:1-4
Lk 9:18-22

Saturday, September 28

WEEKDAY *(Green)*; ST. WENCESLAUS, MARTYR *(Red)*
ST. LAWRENCE RUIZ AND COMPANIONS, MARTYRS *(Red)*
BLESSED VIRGIN MARY *(White)*

"[The LORD said to His people], 'Anyone who strikes you strikes what is most precious to Me.'" (Zech 2:8)

Zech 2:5-9,14-15a
(Ps) Jer 31:10-13
Lk 9:43b-45

NORTHERN ELEPHANT SEAL OFF THE COAST OF CALIFORNIA

"Sin makes God sad, and His Church sad, too, since You are His Church. We are the People of God. When I commit a sin, you all suffer. If you commit a sin, we all suffer. Because of that, I think all sins are tragic."

from *Kiss of Christ: Reflections on the Sacrament of Penance and Reconciliation*

Sunday, September 29

TWENTY-SIXTH SUNDAY IN ORDINARY TIME *(Green)*

"[Christ's] appearing will be brought about at the right time by God, the blessed and only Ruler, the King of kings and the Lord of lords." (1 Tm 6:15)

Am 6:1a,4-7
Ps 146:7-10
1 Tm 6:11-16
Lk 16:19-31

Monday, September 30

ST. JEROME, PRIEST AND DOCTOR *(White)*

"...[Jesus] took a child...and said...'Whoever welcomes this child in My name, welcomes Me...'" (Lk 9:47-48)

Zech 8:1-8
Ps 102:16-21,29,22-23
Lk 9:46-50

Tuesday, October 1

ST. THÉRÈSE OF LISIEUX, VIRGIN AND DOCTOR *(White)*

"The time is coming when...[unbelievers]...will say, 'We want to share in your destiny, because we have heard that God is with you.'" (Zech 8:20-21)

Zech 8:20-23
Ps 87:1-7
Lk 9:51-56

Wednesday, October 2

THE HOLY GUARDIAN ANGELS *(White)*

"'See that you don't despise any of these little ones,' [Jesus said]. 'Their angels...are always in the presence of My Father in heaven.'" (Mt 18:10)

Neh 2:1-8
Ps 137:1-6
Mt 18:1-5,10

Thursday, October 3

WEEKDAY *(Green)*

"Today is holy to our Lord, so don't be sad. The joy that the LORD gives will make you strong." (Neh 8:10c)

Neh 8:1-4a,5-6,7b-12
Ps 19:8-11
Lk 10:1-12

Friday, October 4

ST. FRANCIS OF ASSISI, RELIGIOUS *(White)*

"Jesus said to His disciples, 'Whoever listens to you listens to Me; whoever rejects you rejects Me.'" (Lk 10:16)

Bar 1:15-22
Ps 79:1-3,5,8-9
Lk 10:13-16

Saturday, October 5

WEEKDAY *(Green)*; USA: BL. FRANCIS XAVIER SEELOS, PRIEST *(White)*
BLESSED VIRGIN MARY *(White)*

"The LORD listens to those in need, and does not forget His people..." (Ps 69:33)

Bar 4:5-12,27-29
Ps 69:33-37
Lk 10:17-24

MOUNTAINS IN ARGENTINA, SOUTH AMERICA

"The priest is a mediator between God and humanity – we lay persons, too, must be mediators in our own way. We can 'mediate' by prayer, praying for the whole world. We can mediate, like St. Francis, by being peace-makers – for we are members of Christ's Body and Christ is the Prince of Peace."

from *Mystical Body of Christ*

Sunday, October 6

TWENTY-SEVENTH SUNDAY IN ORDINARY TIME *(Green)*

"The apostles said to the Lord, 'Make our faith greater.'" (Lk 17:5)

Hab 1:2-3; 2:2-4
Ps 95:1-2,6-9
2 Tm 1:6-8,13-14
Lk 17:5-10

Monday, October 7

OUR LADY OF THE ROSARY *(White)*

"Love the Lord your God with all your heart...
soul...strength [and]...mind...and love your
neighbor as you love yourself." (Lk 10:27)

Jon 1:1—2:2,11
(Ps) Jon 2:2-5,8
Lk 10:25-37

Tuesday, October 8

WEEKDAY *(Green)*

"If You kept a record of our sins, [O Lᴏʀᴅ], who
could escape being condemned? But You forgive
us..." (Ps 130:3-4a)

Jon 3:1-10
Ps 130:1-4,7-8
Lk 10:38-42

Wednesday, October 9

WEEKDAY *(Green)*; ST. DENIS, BISHOP AND COMPANIONS, MARTYRS *(Red)*
ST. JOHN LEONARDI, PRIEST *(White)*

"I knew that You are a loving and merciful God,
always patient...kind and...ready to change Your
mind and not punish." (Jon 4:2)

Jon 4:1-11
Ps 86:3-6,9-10
Lk 11:1-4

Thursday, October 10

WEEKDAY *(Green)*

"'For you who obey Me,' [says the LORD
Almighty], 'My saving power will rise on you
like the sun and bring healing like the sun's
rays.'" (Mal 3:20a)

Mal 3:13-20b
Ps 1:1-4,6
Lk 11:5-13

Friday, October 11

WEEKDAY *(Green)*; ST. JOHN XXIII, POPE *(White)*

"[Jesus said], 'Anyone who is not for Me is really against Me...'" (Lk 11:17b)

Jl 1:13-15; 2:1-2
Ps 9:2-3,6,8-9,16
Lk 11:15-26

Saturday, October 12

WEEKDAY *(Green)*; BLESSED VIRGIN MARY *(White)*

"How happy are those who hear the word of God and obey it!" (Lk 11:28)

Jl 4:12-21
Ps 97:1-2,5-6,11-12
Lk 11:27-28

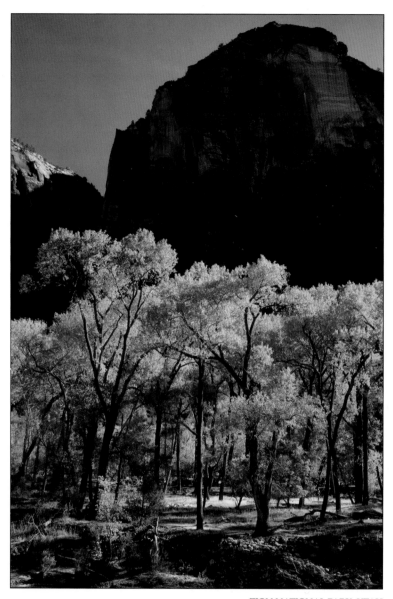

ZION NATIONAL PARK, UTAH

"Lately I am afraid for us Christians. It is as if we are being called to make a last stand, to proclaim the Good News that God has come on earth, that He was born, that He died, and that He resurrected – that He is our Savior. That proclamation today cannot be done only by words. It must be done by living it."

from *Re-entry into Faith*

Sunday, October 13

TWENTY-EIGHTH SUNDAY IN ORDINARY TIME *(Green)*

"If we are not faithful [to Christ], He remains faithful because He cannot be false to Himself."
(2 Tm 2:13)

2 Kgs 5:14-17
Ps 98:1-4
2 Tm 2:8-13
Lk 17:11-19

Monday, October 14

USA: COLUMBUS DAY OBSERVED
CANADA: THANKSGIVING DAY

WEEKDAY *(Green)*
ST. CALLISTUS I, POPE AND MARTYR *(Red)*

"May God our Father and the Lord Jesus Christ give you grace and peace." (Rom 1:7b)

Rom 1:1-7
Ps 98:1-4
Lk 11:29-32

Tuesday, October 15

ST. TERESA OF JESUS, VIRGIN AND DOCTOR *(White)*

"[Those of evil ways] exchange the truth about God for a lie; they worship and serve what God has created instead of the Creator Himself, who is to be praised forever!" (Rom 1:25)

Rom 1:16-25
Ps 19:2-5
Lk 11:37-41

Wednesday, October 16

WEEKDAY *(Green)*; USA: ST. HEDWIG, WIFE AND RELIGIOUS *(White)*
USA: ST. MARGARET MARY ALACOQUE, VIRGIN *(White)*
CANADA: ST. MARGUERITE D'YOUVILLE, RELIGIOUS *(White)*

"God will reward each of us according to what we have done." (Rom 2:6)

Rom 2:1-11
Ps 62:2-3,6-7,9
Lk 11:42-46

Thursday, October 17

ST. IGNATIUS OF ANTIOCH, BISHOP AND MARTYR *(Red)*

"From the depths of my despair I call to You, LORD. Hear my cry." (Ps 130:1-2)

Rom 3:21-30
Ps 130:1-6
Lk 11:47-54

Friday, October 18

ST. LUKE, EVANGELIST *(Red)*

"'Go!' [Jesus said], 'I am sending you like lambs among wolves.'" (Lk 10:3)

2 Tm 4:10-17b
Ps 145:10-13,17-18
Lk 10:1-9

Saturday, October 19

USA: STS. ISAAC JOGUES AND JOHN DE BRÉBEUF, PRIESTS
   AND COMPANIONS, MARTYRS *(Red)*
CANADA: ST. PAUL OF THE CROSS, PRIEST *(White)*

"...those who declare publicly that they belong to Me, the Son of Man will do the same for them before the angels of God." (Lk 12:8)

Rom 4:13,16-18
Ps 105:6-9,42-43
Lk 12:8-12

GRAND TETON NATIONAL PARK, WYOMING

"What does poverty of spirit really mean...? It means, first of all, utter detachment from all created goods. It means a deep, lasting realization that all created things, which include father, mother, children, relatives and friends, as well as money, house and goods are given to us by God as means to one end, which is sanctity. Without sanctity we shall not achieve the primary end for which we were created – the beatific vision, to see God 'face to face' (1 Cor 13:12)."

from *Nazareth Family Spirituality*

Sunday, October 20

TWENTY-NINTH SUNDAY IN ORDINARY TIME *(Green)*

"Jesus told His disciples...that they should always pray and never become discouraged." (Lk 18:1)

Ex 17:8-13
Ps 121:1-8
2 Tm 3:14—4:2
Lk 18:1-8

Monday, October 21

WEEKDAY *(Green)*

"Because of our sins [Jesus] was given over to die, but He was raised to life in order to put us right with God." (Rom 4:25)

Rom 4:20-25
(Ps) Lk 1: 69-75
Lk 12:13-21

Tuesday, October 22

WEEKDAY *(Green)*; ST. JOHN PAUL II, POPE *(White)*
CANADA: DEDICATION OF CHURCHES *(White)*

"I am weak and poor, O LORD, but You have not forgotten me; ...hurry to my aid!" (Ps 40:17)

Rom 5:12,15b,17-19,20b-21
Ps 40:7-10,17
Lk 12:35-38

Wednesday, October 23

WEEKDAY *(Green)*; ST. JOHN OF CAPISTRANO, PRIEST *(White)*

"Much is required from the person to whom much is given." (Lk 12:48b)

Rom 6:12-18
Ps 124:1-8
Lk12:39-48

Thursday, October 24

WEEKDAY *(Green)*; ST. ANTHONY CLARET, BISHOP *(White)*

"Sin pays its wage—death; but God's free gift is eternal life in union with Christ Jesus." (Rom 6:23)

Rom 6:19-23
Ps 1:1-4,6
Lk 12:49-53

Friday, October 25

WEEKDAY *(Green)*

"Give me wisdom and knowledge, [O LORD],
because I trust in Your commands." (Ps 119:66)

Rom 7:18-25a
Ps 119:66,68,76-77,93-94
Lk 12:54-59

Saturday, October 26

WEEKDAY *(Green)*; BLESSED VIRGIN MARY *(White)*

"The world and all that is in it belong to the
LORD; the earth and all who live on it are His."
(Ps 24:1)

Rom 8:1-11
Ps 24:1-6
Lk 13:1-9

SUNRISE OVER NORTHERN MANITOBA, CANADA

"Beloved, You are the light and the life of my soul. Teach me to follow You."

from *O Jesus: Prayers from the Diaries of Catherine DeHueck Doherty*

Sunday, October 27

THIRTIETH SUNDAY IN ORDINARY TIME *(Green)*

"Those who make themselves great will be humbled, and those who humble themselves will be made great." (Lk 18:14b)

Sir 35:12-14,16-18
Ps 34:2-3,17-19,23
2 Tm 4:6-8,16-18
Lk 18:9-14

ORDER FORM

To order copies of *Listen to the Spirit—He Will Lead You 2020 Prayer Journal*, please use the order blank printed below.

TRINITY PHOTOGRAPHY
3805 7th St. NE #109
Great Falls, MT 59404-1154
<u>OR</u>

PHONE orders: **1-888-220-5941** (toll free)
E-MAIL orders: **catholicprayerdiary@gmail.com**
ONLINE orders: **www.catholicprayerdiary.com**

<u>COST in U.S. DOLLARS</u>

<u>**U.S.A.**</u>   **1 - 5** journals . . . . **$16.99** each
6 - 9 journals . . . . **$15.99** each
10 or more journals . . . **$14.99** each

***** *WE **PAY** THE **SHIPPING** within the* **U.S.*!!!*** *****

<u>CANADA</u>   Contact: **Madonna House Publications**,
2888 Dafoe Rd., RR #2, Combermere, Ontario K0J 1L0
1-888-703-7110 (toll free)
publications@madonnahouse.org
Madonna House has its own pricing and shipping policies.

I order _____ journal(s) at _____ each. *TOTAL: $*_____

Method of Payment: ___ **Check**   ___ **Money Order**   ___ **Discover**

___**Visa** ___**Mastercard - Card#**_____

Expires _____ **Security #s**_____ **Sign**_____
(3 digits on back of card)   (as your name appears on your card)

(Please <u>PRINT</u>)

Send to _____

Address _____

_____

City_____State_____

Zip Code_____Phone _____
(required for credit card purchases)

(Allow 2-3 weeks for delivery)

THANK YOU FOR YOUR ORDER!

TO ORDER PHOTOGRAPHS

If you would like to order prints of any of the photographs included in this calendar, or to inquire about obtaining permission to use any of them in your own publication, please contact Trinity Photography contact person, Sandy Wedel, to discuss size, finish, and other specifications, as well as to obtain prices.

Write: **ATTN: Sandy Wedel**
Trinity Photography
3805 7th St. NE #109
Great Falls, MT 59404-1154

Phone: **1-888-220-5941**

E-Mail: **catholicprayerdiary@gmail.com**

Please include **your name** and **phone number** in any type of correspondence.

Monday, October 28

STS. SIMON AND JUDE, APOSTLES *(Red)*

"In union with [Christ Jesus] you too are being built together with all the others into [the household of God] where God lives through His Spirit." (Eph 2:22)

Eph 2:19-22
Ps 19:2-5
Lk 6:12-16

Tuesday, October 29

WEEKDAY *(Green)*

"I consider that what we suffer at this present time cannot be compared at all with the glory that is going to be revealed to us." (Rom 8:18)

Rom 8:18-25
Ps 126:1-6
Lk 13:18-21

Wednesday, October 30

WEEKDAY *(Green)*

"We do not know how we ought to pray; the Spirit Himself pleads with God for us in groans that words cannot express." (Rom 8:26)

Rom 8:26-30
Ps 13:4-6
Lk 13:22-30

Thursday, October 31 HALLOWEEN

WEEKDAY *(Green)*

"If God is for us, who can be against us?" (Rom 8:31b)

Rom 8:31b-39
Ps 109:21-22,26-27,30-31
Lk13:31-35

Friday, November 1 *HOLY DAY OF OBLIGATION*

ALL SAINTS *(White)*

"Happy are the pure in heart; they will see God!" (Mt 5:8)

Rv 7:2-4,9-14
Ps 24:1-6
1 Jn 3:1-3
Mt 5:1-12a

Saturday, November 2 ALL SOULS DAY

THE COMMEMORATION OF ALL THE FAITHFUL DEPARTED *(White, Violet or Black)*

"[Jesus said], 'I will never turn away anyone who comes to Me.'" (Jn 6:37b)

Wis 3:1-9
Ps 27:1,4,7-9,13-14
Rom 5:5-11 or 6:3-9
Jn 6:37-40

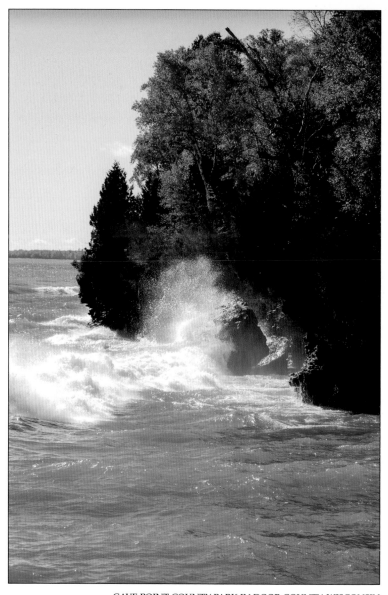

CAVE POINT COUNTY PARK IN DOOR COUNTY, WISCONSIN

"It is said of fear that it exists to be overcome..."

from *In the Furnace of Doubts: Meditations—when you've lost your answers*

Sunday, November 3

THIRTY-FIRST SUNDAY IN ORDINARY TIME *(Green)*

"...You gently correct those who sin...so that they may abandon their evil ways and put their trust in You, Lord." (Wis 12:2)

Wis 11:22—12:2
Ps 145:1-2,8-11,13-14
2 Thes 1:11—2:2
Lk 19:1-10

Monday, November 4

ST. CHARLES BORROMEO, BISHOP *(White)*

"How deep are [God's] wisdom and knowledge! Who can explain His decisions? Who can understand His ways?" (Rom 11:33bcd)

Rom 11:29-36
Ps 69:30-31,33-34,36-37
Lk 14:12-14

Tuesday, November 5

WEEKDAY *(Green)*

"How happy are those who will sit down at the feast in the Kingdom of God!" (Lk 14:15b)

Rom 12:5-16b
Ps 131:1-3
Lk 14:15-24

Wednesday, November 6

WEEKDAY *(Green)*

"If you love others, you will never do them wrong; to love, then, is to obey the whole Law." (Rom 13:10)

Rom 13:8-10
Ps 112:1-2,4-5,9
Lk 14:25-33

Thursday, November 7

WEEKDAY *(Green)*

"'As surely as I am the living God,' says the Lord, 'everyone will kneel before Me, and everyone will confess that I am God.'" (Rom 14:11)

Rom 14:7-12
Ps 27:1,4,13-14
Lk 15:1-10

Friday, November 8

WEEKDAY *(Green)*

"Sing a new song to the LORD; He has done wonderful things!" (Ps 98:1a)

Rom 15:14-21
Ps 98:1-4
Lk 16:1-8

Saturday, November 9

DEDICATION OF THE ST. JOHN LATERAN BASILICA *(White)*

"God has already placed Jesus Christ as the one and only foundation [for His church], and no other foundation can be laid." (1 Cor 3:11)

Ez 47:1-2,8-9,12
Ps 84:3-6,8,11
1 Cor 3:9c-11,16-17
Jn 2:13-22

AN ALLIGATOR IN EVERGLADES NATIONAL PARK, FLORIDA

"I am at the sacrament of confession in Russia. The first question this old priest asks me is, 'Child, how much do you love your enemies?' I was very puzzled, I didn't know I had enemies. So he said, 'Maybe now you have none, but in the future you will. Always examine your conscience as to how you love your enemies. For only if you love them well are you fulfilling God's commandment of love.'"

from *An Experience of God*

Sunday, November 10 *Daylight Savings Time Ends*

THIRTY-SECOND SUNDAY IN ORDINARY TIME *(Green)*

"May our Lord Jesus Christ Himself and God
our Father...encourage you and strengthen you to
always do and say what is good." (2 Thes 2:16)

2 Mac 7:1-2,9-14
Ps 17:1,5-6,8,15
2 Thes 2:16—3:5
Lk 20:27-38

Monday, November 11
USA: VETERAN'S DAY
CANADA: REMEMBRANCE DAY

ST. MARTIN OF TOURS, BISHOP *(White)*

"[Holy people] will not feel comfortable when injustice is done." (Wis 1:5c)

Wis 1:1-7
Ps 139:1-10
Lk 17:1-6

Tuesday, November 12

ST. JOSAPHAT, BISHOP AND MARTYR *(Red)*

"Those who have put their trust in God will come to understand the truth of His ways." (Wis 3:9)

Wis 2:23—3:9
Ps 34:2-3,16-19
Lk 17:7-10

Wednesday, November 13

USA: ST. FRANCES XAVIER CABRINI, VIRGIN *(White)*

"[The Lord] Himself made everyone, great and common alike, and He provides for all equally, but He will judge the conduct of rulers more strictly." (Wis 6:7-8)

Wis 6:1-11
Ps 82:3-4,6-7
Lk 17:11-19

Thursday, November 14

WEEKDAY *(Green)*

"[Wisdom] loves what is good. It is sharp and unconquerable, kind, and a friend of humanity." (Wis 7:22f-23a)

Wis 7:22b—8:1
Ps 119:89-91,130,135,175
Lk 17:20-25

Friday, November 15

WEEKDAY *(Green)*
ST. ALBERT THE GREAT, BISHOP AND DOCTOR *(White)*

"When we realize how vast and beautiful the creation is, we are learning about the Creator at the same time." (Wis 13:5)

Wis 13:1-9
Ps 19:2-5
Lk 17:26-37

Saturday, November 16

WEEKDAY *(Green)*
ST. MARGARET OF SCOTLAND, WIFE, MOTHER, QUEEN *(White)*
ST. GERTRUDE, VIRGIN *(White)*; BLESSED VIRGIN MARY, *(White)*

"Will the Son of Man find faith on earth when He comes?" (Lk 18:8b)

Wis 18:14-16; 19:6-9
Ps 105:2-3,36-37,42-43
Lk 18:1-8

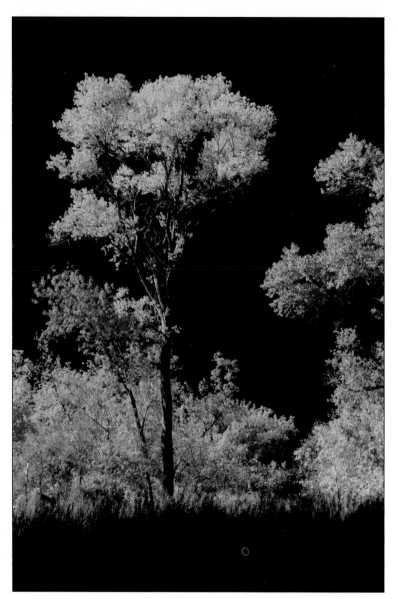

ZION NATIONAL PARK, UTAH

"I foresee that we may have to face that we are in the minority, and in the midst of that minority Christ stands, asking us not to be afraid, not to be worried, because He – in fact, the Trinity, Father, Son and Holy Spirit – is really renewing the Church and the people of God. The Church has gone through many tremendous and difficult periods. Do not imagine that it will not survive this current period." *from Mystical Body of Christ*

Sunday, November 17

THIRTY-THIRD SUNDAY IN ORDINARY TIME *(Green)*

"Watch out; don't be fooled. Many men, claiming to speak for Me [Jesus] will come and say, 'I am he!' ...but don't follow them." (Lk 21:8)

Mal 3:19-20a
Ps 98:5-9
2 Thes 3:7-12
Lk 21:5-19

Monday, November 18

WEEKDAY (Green)
DEDICATION OF THE BASILICAS OF STS. PETER AND PAUL (White)
USA: ST. ROSE PHILIPPINE DUCHESNE, VIRGIN, (White)

"When I see the wicked breaking Your law,
[O LORD], I am filled with anger." (Ps 119:53)

1 Mac 1:10-15,41-43,54-57,62-63
Ps 119:53,61,134,150,155,158
Lk 18:35-43

Tuesday, November 19

WEEKDAY (Green)

"The Son of Man came to seek and to save the
lost." (Lk 19:10)

2 Mac 6:18-31
Ps 3:2-8
Lk 19:1-10

Wednesday, November 20

WEEKDAY *(Green)*

"[The mother said], 'I was not the one who gave you life and breath and put together each part of your body. It was God who did it...'" (2 Mac 7:22b-23a)

2 Mac 7:1,20-31
Ps 17:1,5-6,8,15
Lk 19:11-28

Thursday, November 21

PRESENTATION OF THE BLESSED VIRGIN MARY *(White)*

"With God's help we will never abandon His Law or disobey His commands." (1 Mac 2:21)

1 Mac 2:15-29
Ps 50:1-2,5-6,14-15
Lk 19:41-44

Friday, November 22

ST. CECILIA, VIRGIN AND MARTYR *(Red)*

"...all the people kept listening to [Jesus], not wanting to miss a single word." (Lk 19:48b)

1 Mac 4:36-37,52-59
(Ps) 1 Chr 29:10-12
Lk 19:45-48

Saturday, November 23

WEEKDAY *(Green)*; ST. CLEMENT I, POPE AND MARTYR *(Red)*
ST. COLUMBAN, ABBOT *(White)*
USA: BLESSED MIGUEL AGUSTÍN PRO, PRIEST AND MARTYR *(Red)*

"[God] is the God of the living, not of the dead, for to Him all are alive." (Lk 20:38)

1 Mac 6:1-13
Ps 9:2-4,6,16,19
Lk 20:27-40

SKY OVER MONTANA

"The pity of God is immense and profound. It is like a fresh wind that comes up suddenly on a torrid day. It is like a cool evening when the sky is pink and blue and red and beautiful to behold... If we let God's pity penetrate the deepest levels of our being...so many of our inner hurts, fears and negative emotions can be assuaged."

from *God in the Nitty Gritty Life*

Sunday, November 24

OUR LORD JESUS CHRIST, KING OF THE UNIVERSE *(White)*

"With joy give thanks to the Father, who has made you fit to have your share of what God has reserved for His people in the kingdom of light." (Col 1:12)

2 Sam 5:1-3
Ps 122:1-5
Col 1:12-20
Lk 23:35-43

Monday, November 25

WEEKDAY *(Green)*
ST. CATHERINE OF ALEXANDRIA, VIRGIN AND MARTYR *(Red)*

"[O LORD], may You be praised as You sit on
Your royal throne. May hymns be sung to Your
glory forever." (Dan 3:54)

Dan 1:1-6,8-20
(Ps) Dan 3:52-56
Lk 21:1-4

Tuesday, November 26

WEEKDAY *(Green)*

"Jesus said, '...don't be fooled. Many...claiming
to speak for Me will come... But don't follow
them.'" (Lk 21:8)

Dan 2:31-45
(Ps) Dan 3:57-61
Lk 21:5-11

Wednesday, November 27

WEEKDAY *(Green)*

"'Stand firm and you will save yourselves,'
[Jesus said]." (Lk 21:19)

Dan 5:1-6,13-14,16-17,23-28
(Ps) Dan 3:62-67
Lk 21:12-19

Thursday, November 28   USA: THANKSGIVING DAY

WEEKDAY *(Green)*
USA: THANKSGIVING DAY RITUAL MASS *(White)*

"In union with Christ you have become rich in
all things..." (1 Cor 1:5a)

Weekday Mass:	**Thanksgiving Mass:**
Dan 6:12-28	Sir 50:22-24
(Ps) Dan 3:68-74	Ps 67:2-3,5,7-8
Lk 21:20-28	1 Cor 1:3-9
	Lk 17:11-19

Friday, November 29

WEEKDAY *(Green)*

"'Heaven and earth will pass away,' [Jesus told them], 'but My words will never pass away.'"
(Lk 21:33)

Dan 7:2-14
(Ps) Dan 3:75-81
Lk 21:29-33

Saturday, November 30

ST. ANDREW, APOSTLE *(Red)*

"The scripture says, 'Whoever believes in [Christ Jesus] will not be disappointed.'" (Rom 10:11)

Rom 10:9-18
Ps 19:2-5
Mt 4:18-22

EMPEROR PENGUINS ON SOUTH GEORGIA ISLAND

"[To love others with God's heart] is the answer to all the questioning, confusion, turmoil and unrest which are presently shaking us like bruised reeds. First, foremost, and last, before we talk about techniques, sensitivity courses, interpersonal relationships and all the rest, we must ask ourselves the following question: Have we begun to love the people in the community in which God has placed us? It may be a family ... a religious community, the parish ... a neighborhood. Have we begun to love the people with whom we live? Have I begun to be concerned, not about myself, but about everyone else?"

from *Light in the Darkness: A Christian Vision for Unstable Times*

Sunday, December 1

FIRST SUNDAY OF ADVENT *(Violet)*

"...the time has come for you to wake up from your sleep. For the moment when we will be saved is closer now than it was when we first believed." (Rom 13:11)

Is 2:1-5
Ps 122:1-9
Rom 13:11-14
Mt 24:37-44

Monday, December 2

ADVENT WEEKDAY *(Violet)*

"By His power the Lord will judge and purify the nation..." (Is 4:4a)

Is 4:2-6
Ps 122:1-9
Mt 8:5-11

Tuesday, December 3

ST. FRANCIS XAVIER, PRIEST *(White)*

"[The LORD] has pity on the weak and poor; He saves the lives of those in need." (Ps 72:13)

Is 11:1-10
Ps 72:1,7-8,12-13,17
Lk 10:21-24

Wednesday, December 4

ADVENT WEEKDAY *(Violet)*
ST. JOHN DAMASCENE, PRIEST AND DOCTOR *(White)*

"...the LORD Almighty will prepare...a banquet of the richest food and the finest wine." (Is 25:6)

Is 25:6-10a
Ps 23:1-6
Mt 15:29-37

Thursday, December 5

ADVENT WEEKDAY *(Violet)*

"Save us, LORD, save us!" (Ps 118:25a)

Is 26:1-6
Ps 118:1,8-9,19-21,25-27
Mt 7:21,24-27

Friday, December 6

ADVENT WEEKDAY *(Violet)*
ST. NICHOLAS, BISHOP *(White)*

"Trust in the LORD. Have faith, do not despair.
Trust in the LORD." (Ps 27:14)

Is 29:17-24
Ps 27:1-4,13-14
Mt 9:27-31

Saturday, December 7

ST. AMBROSE, BISHOP AND DOCTOR *(White)*

"The LORD will make you go through hard times,
but He Himself will be there to teach you, and
you will not have to search for Him any more."
(Is 30:20b)

Is 30:19-21,23-26
Ps 147:1-6
Mt 9:35—10:1,5a,6-8

SUNRISE IN NAMIBIA, AFRICA

"This is something to really pray about. Can anybody see the light of Christ through our eyes? Through our speech? Through our behavior? Do we wish to remain darkness, and, by doing so, keep others in darkness, too?"

from *Re-entry into Faith*

Sunday, December 8

SECOND SUNDAY OF ADVENT *(Violet)*

"Someone is shouting in the desert, 'Prepare a road for the Lord; make a straight path for Him to travel.'" (Mt 3:3)

Is 11:1-10
Ps 72:1-2,7-8,12-13,17
Rom 15:4-9
Mt 3:1-12

Monday, December 9 NOT A HOLY DAY OF OBLIGATION THIS YEAR

IMMACULATE CONCEPTION OF THE BLESSED VIRGIN MARY, *(White)*
Patronal Feastday of the USA

"Even before the world was made, God had already chosen us to be His through our union with Christ..." (Eph 1:4a)

Gen 3:9-15,20
Ps 98:1-4
Eph 1:3-6,11-12
Lk 1:26-38

Tuesday, December 10

ADVENT WEEKDAY *(Violet)*

"Grass withers and flowers fade, but the word of our God endures forever." (Is 40:8)

Is 40:1-11
Ps 96:1-3,10-13
Mt 18:12-14

Wednesday, December 11

ADVENT WEEKDAY *(Violet)*
ST. DAMASUS I, POPE *(White)*

"The LORD is the everlasting God; He created
all the world. He never grows tired or weary."
(Is 40:28)

Is 40:25-31
Ps 103:1-4,8,10
Mt 11:28-30

Thursday, December 12

OUR LADY OF GUADALUPE *(White)*
  Patroness of the Americas

"[Mary said], 'From now on all people will call
me happy, because of the great things the Mighty
God has done for me.'" (Lk 1:48b-49a)

Zech 2:14-17 or Rv 11:19a; 12:1-6a,10ab
(Ps) Lk 1:46-55
Lk 1:26-38 or Lk 1:39-47

Friday, December 13

ST. LUCY, VIRGIN AND MARTYR *(Red)*

"God's wisdom...is shown to be true by its results." (Mt 11:19c)

Is 48:17-19
Ps 1:1-4,6
Mt 11:16-19

Saturday, December 14

ST. JOHN OF THE CROSS, PRIEST AND DOCTOR *(White)*

"[O Shepherd of Israel]...show us Your strength and save us." (Ps 80:2)

Sir 48:1-4,9-11
Ps 80:2-3,15-16,18-19
Mt 17:9a,10-13

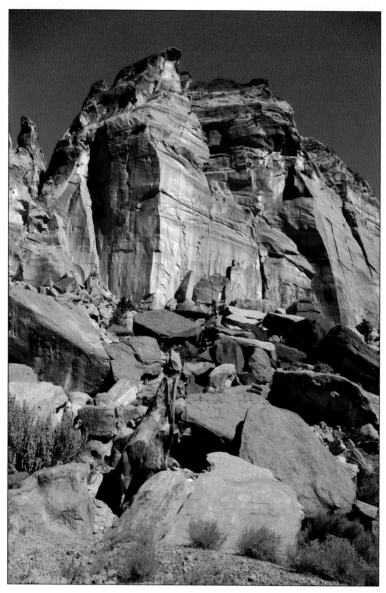

ARCHES NATIONAL PARK, UTAH

"We Christians must break down all the invisible walls of the past that kept us from being a sign of love. As our love for one another becomes evident, spilling over into every corner of our world, when we all are a sign of love – then those who do not belong to [the Church's] community of faith and worship may wish to do so, for we will have incarnated God's word and our love will be palpable and visible." from *Mystical Body of Christ*

Sunday, December 15

THIRD SUNDAY OF ADVENT *(Violet or Rose)*

"My friends, remember the prophets who spoke in the name of the Lord. Take them as examples of patient endurance under suffering." (Jas 5:10)

Is 35:1-6a,10
Ps 146:6-10
Jas 5:7-10
Mt 11:2-11

Monday, December 16

ADVENT WEEKDAY *(Violet)*

"Teach me to live according to Your truth, for You are my God, who saves me." (Ps 25:5ab)

Num 24:2-7,15-17a
Ps 25:4-9
Mt 21:23-27

Tuesday, December 17

ADVENT WEEKDAY *(Violet)*

"May all nations ask God to bless them..." (Ps 72:17c)

Gen 49:2,8-10
Ps 72:3-4,7-8,17
Mt 1:1-17

Wednesday, December 18

ADVENT WEEKDAY *(Violet)*

"[Mary] will have a son, and you [Joseph] will name Him Jesus—because He will save His people from their sins." (Mt 1:21)

Jer 23:5-8
Ps 72:1,12-13,18-19
Mt 1:18-25

Thursday, December 19

ADVENT WEEKDAY *(Violet)*

"Sovereign LORD, I put my hope in You." (Ps 71:5a)

Jgs 13:2-7,24-25a
Ps 71:3-6,16-17
Lk 1:5-25

Friday, December 20

ADVENT WEEKDAY *(Violet)*

"The Holy Spirit will come on you, [Mary], and God's power will rest upon you. For this reason the holy child will be called the Son of God." (Lk 1:35)

Is 7:10-14
Ps 24:1-6
Lk 1:26-38

Saturday, December 21

ADVENT WEEKDAY *(Violet)*
ST. PETER CANISIUS, PRIEST AND DOCTOR

"The LORD your God is with you; His power gives you victory. The LORD will take delight in you, and in His love He will give you new life." (Zeph 3:17)

Sg 2:8-14 or Zeph 3:14-18a
Ps 33:2-3,11-12,20-21
Lk 1:39-45

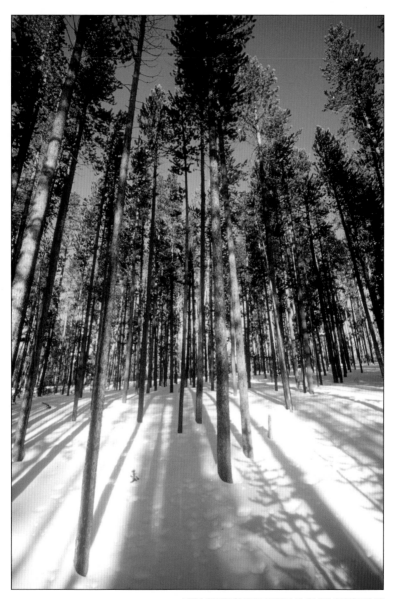

YELLOWSTONE NATIONAL PARK, WYOMING

"Truly He is worthy of our love. Nothing on earth or in heaven matters except God. See how He comes to us in a wooden manger, proclaiming His love even before He can speak our language. Notice the wood in the manger. How He loves wood! He chose it as a crib, and then He chose to work with it as a carpenter. Finally, He died on wood. All this for love of us."

from *Grace in Every Season: Through the Year with Catherine Doherty*

Sunday, December 22 *First Day of Winter*

FOURTH SUNDAY OF ADVENT *(Violet)*

"A virgin will become pregnant and have a son, and He will be called Immanuel (which means 'God is with us')." (Mt 1:23)

Is 7:10-14
Ps 24:1-6
Rom 1:1-7
Mt 1:18-24

Monday, December 23

ADVENT WEEKDAY *(Violet)*
ST. JOHN OF KANTY, PRIEST

"The LORD is the friend of those who obey Him
and He affirms His covenant with them."
(Ps 25:14)

Mal 3:1-4,23-24
Ps 25:4-5,8-10,14
Lk 1:57-66

Tuesday, December 24 CHRISTMAS EVE

ADVENT WEEKDAY *(Violet)*

"Let us praise the Lord, the God of Israel! He has
come to the help of His people and has set them
free." (Lk 1:68)

2 Sam 7:1-5,8b-12,14a,16
Ps 89:2-5,27,29
Lk 1:67-79
Vigil of Christmas Readings: see Appendix

Wednesday, December 25 CHRISTMAS HOLY DAY OF OBLIGATION

THE NATIVITY OF THE LORD *(White)*

"The Word...brought light to mankind. The Light shines in the darkness, and the darkness has never put it out." (Jn 1:4-5)

Readings: see Appendix

Thursday, December 26 CANADA: BOXING DAY

ST. STEPHEN, THE FIRST MARTYR *(Red)*

"They kept on stoning Stephen as he called out to the Lord, 'Lord Jesus, receive my spirit!'" (Acts 7:59)

Acts 6:8-10; 7:54-59
Ps 31:3-4,6-8,17,21
Mt 10:17-22

Friday, December 27

ST. JOHN, APOSTLE AND EVANGELIST *(White)*

"...join...in the fellowship that we have with the Father and with His Son Jesus Christ." (1 Jn 1:3b)

1 Jn 1:1-4
Ps 97:1-2,5-6,11-12
Jn 20:1a,2-8

Saturday, Thursday 28

HOLY INNOCENTS, MARTYRS *(Red)*

"If we say that we have fellowship with [God], yet at the same time live in the darkness, we are lying both in our words and in our actions." (1 Jn 1:6)

1 Jn 1:5—2:2
Ps 124:2-5,7-8
Mt 2:13-18

EMPEROR PENGUINS ON SNOW HILL ISLAND, ANTARCTICA

"Our society is increasingly secular, depersonalized and dehumanized. In many instances the relationship is more to a machine than to people. The relationship is with TV, computer, with machines of one type or another, and interpersonal relationships are thus diminished. In our person and as a family, we can be a refuge against the dehumanization of the world."

from *Living the Gospel without Compromise*

Sunday, December 29

THE HOLY FAMILY OF JESUS, MARY AND JOSEPH *(White)*

"Be tolerant with one another and forgive one another whenever any of you has a complaint against someone else." (Col 3:13)

Sir 3:2-6,12-14
Ps 128:1-5
Col 3:12-21
Mt 2:13-15,19-23

Monday, December 30

SIXTH DAY WITHIN THE OCTAVE OF CHRISTMAS *(White)*

"The world and everything in it that people desire is passing away; but those who do the will of God live forever." (1 Jn 2:17)

1 Jn 2:12-17
Ps 96:7-10
Lk 2:36-40

Tuesday, December 31 NEW YEAR'S EVE

SEVENTH DAY WITHIN THE OCTAVE OF CHRISTMAS *(White)*
ST. SYLVESTER I, POPE

"Out of the fullness of [the Word's] grace He has blessed us all, giving us one blessing after another." (Jn 1:16)

1 Jn 2:18-21
Ps 96:1-2,11-13
Jn 1:1-18

APPENDIX

DAY OF PRAYER FOR THE LEGAL PROTECTION OF UNBORN CHILDREN (January 22), any of the following:

Gen 1:1—2:2 or 2 Mac 7:1,20-31 or Is 49:1-6 or Rom 11:33-36 or
    Eph 1:3-14 or Eph 3:14-21 or Col 1:12-20 or 1 Jn 3:11-21
Mt 18:1-5,10,12-14 or Mk 9:30-37 or Lk 1:39-56 or Lk 17:11-19
    or Lk 23:35-43 or Jn 1:1-5,9-14,16-18 or Jn 6:24-35

ASCENSION OF THE LORD (May 30 or June 2)

The ecclesiastical provinces of Boston, Hartford, New York, Newark, Omaha, and Philadelphia have kept the celebration of the Solemnity of the Ascension on a Thursday (this year May 30), and IT IS A HOLY DAY OF OBLIGATION in those provinces. All other provinces, and all of Canada, have transferred it to the Seventh Sunday of Easter (this year June 2). In those provinces and Canada, Thursday, May 30, is NOT a holy day of obligation.

EASTER VIGIL (April 20)

Gen 1:1—2:2 (Ps 104:1-2,5-6,10,12-14,24,35)
Gen 22:1-18 (Ps 16:5,8,9-10,11)
Ex 14:15—15:1 (Ps - Ex 15:1-2,3-4,5-6,17-18)
Is 54:5-14 (Ps 30:2,4,5-6,11-12,13)
Is 55:1-11 (Ps - Is 12:2-3,4,5-6)
Bar 3:9-15,32—4:4 (Ps 19:8,9,10,11)
Ez 36:16-17a,18-28 (Ps 42:3,5; 43:3,4)
Rom 6:3-11 (Ps 118:1-2,16-17,22-23)
Lk 24:1-12

CHRISTMAS (December 24 and 25)

<u>Vigil Mass</u> (12/24)
Is 62:1-5
Ps 89:4-5,16-17,27,29
Acts 13:16-17,22-25
Mt 1:1-25

<u>Midnight Mass</u> (12/25)
Is 9:1-6
Ps 96:1-3,11-13
Ti 2:11-14
Lk 2:1-14

<u>Mass at Dawn</u> (12/25)
Is 62:11-12
Ps 97:1,6,11-12
Ti 3:4-7
Lk 2:15-20

<u>Mass during the Day</u> (12/25)
Is 52:7-10
Ps 98:1-6
Heb 1:1-6
Jn 1:1-18

2020

JANUARY

S	M	T	W	T	F	S
			1	2	3	4
5	6	7	8	9	10	11
12	13	14	15	16	17	18
19	20	21	22	23	24	25
26	27	28	29	30	31	

FEBRUARY

S	M	T	W	T	F	S
						1
2	3	4	5	6	7	8
9	10	11	12	13	14	15
16	17	18	19	20	21	22
23	24	25	26	27	28	29

MARCH

S	M	T	W	T	F	S
1	2	3	4	5	6	7
8	9	10	11	12	13	14
15	16	17	18	19	20	21
22	23	24	25	26	27	28
29	30	31				

APRIL

S	M	T	W	T	F	S
			1	2	3	4
5	6	7	8	9	10	11
12	13	14	15	16	17	18
19	20	21	22	23	24	25
26	27	28	29	30		

MAY

S	M	T	W	T	F	S
					1	2
3	4	5	6	7	8	9
10	11	12	13	14	15	16
17	18	19	20	21	22	23
24	25	26	27	28	29	30
31						

JUNE

S	M	T	W	T	F	S
	1	2	3	4	5	6
7	8	9	10	11	12	13
14	15	16	17	18	19	20
21	22	23	24	25	26	27
28	29	30				

JULY

S	M	T	W	T	F	S
			1	2	3	4
5	6	7	8	9	10	11
12	13	14	15	16	17	18
19	20	21	22	23	24	25
26	27	28	29	30	31	

AUGUST

S	M	T	W	T	F	S
						1
2	3	4	5	6	7	8
9	10	11	12	13	14	15
16	17	18	19	20	21	22
23	24	25	26	27	28	29
30	31					

SEPTEMBER

S	M	T	W	T	F	S
		1	2	3	4	5
6	7	8	9	10	11	12
13	14	15	16	17	18	19
20	21	22	23	24	25	26
27	28	29	30			

OCTOBER

S	M	T	W	T	F	S
				1	2	3
4	5	6	7	8	9	10
11	12	13	14	15	16	17
18	19	20	21	22	23	24
25	26	27	28	29	30	31

NOVEMBER

S	M	T	W	T	F	S
1	2	3	4	5	6	7
8	9	10	11	12	13	14
15	16	17	18	19	20	21
22	23	24	25	26	27	28
29	30					

DECEMBER

S	M	T	W	T	F	S
		1	2	3	4	5
6	7	8	9	10	11	12
13	14	15	16	17	18	19
20	21	22	23	24	25	26
27	28	29	30	31		